Student Solutions Manual
for

David S. Moore, William I. Notz, and Michael A. Fligner's
The Basic Practice of Statistics

Seventh Edition

Patricia Humphrey
Georgia Southern University

W. H. Freeman and Company
A Macmillan Education Company
New York

© 2015 by W. H. Freeman and Company

ISBN-13: 978-1-4641-7989-1
ISBN-10: 1-4641-7989-1

Printed in the United States of America.

First Printing 2015

W. H. Freeman and Company
41 Madison Avenue
New York, NY 10010
Houndmills, Basingstoke RG21 6XS, England
www.whfreeman.com

CONTENTS

Chapter 0 – Getting Started

0.1 (a) More than likely, the individuals who chose to take Vitamin E were more health-conscious in general than those who didn't take it. They may also have been more affluent (i.e., had money available to purchase the vitamins and possibly better health care generally). **(b)** In a randomized experiment, people of all types are randomly assigned to the treatments. This means that poorer, less healthy people are in both treatment groups, as are the wealthier, healthier people.

0.3 (a) The proportion of Americans who feel this way is very likely much lower. The "survey" was one of voluntary response (i.e., people were not randomly selected, but made their own decision to participate or not). Those who knew about the "poll" had just watched Mr. Schultz's "lengthy and impassioned" monologue and were primed to agree with him. **(b)** As long as the poll was a voluntary response, the sample size (868, 2500, or 100,000) doesn't matter; it's a biased sample and will not reflect the views of people nationwide.

Chapter 1 – Picturing Distributions with Graphs

1.1 (a) The individuals are the car makes and models. **(b)** For each individual, the variables recorded are Vehicle class (categorical), Transmission type (categorical), Number of cylinders (usually treated as quantitative), City mpg (quantitative), Highway mpg (quantitative), and Annual fuel cost (dollars, quantitative).

1.3 (a) The given shares sum to 76.4%. 100% − 76.4% = 23.6% of the radio audience listens to stations with other formats. **(b)** The bar graph is shown at right. **(c)** A pie chart would be inappropriate based only on the data presented because the areas of the pie wedges would be relative to the total of the categories presented (76.4%). If you include a wedge for "Other format" that accounts for 23.6% of the total, a pie chart would be reasonable.

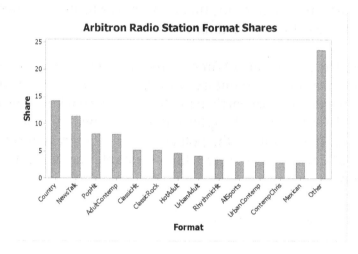

1.5 A pie chart would make it more difficult to distinguish between the weekend days and the weekdays. Some births are scheduled (induced labor, for example), and probably most are scheduled for weekdays.

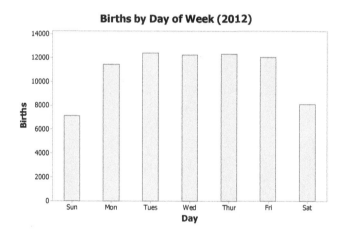

1.7 Use the applet to answer these questions.

1.9 (a) There are two clear peaks in the distribution. If we gave only one center, it would most likely be between these, and not be truly representative. **(b)** Young boys might spend a lot of time outdoors playing and engaged in sports; their time outside in places where they would encounter ticks might well be less as they go through the college age and younger adulthood. With families and yard work, their time outside might increase. **(c)** This is wrong. Hiking in the woods at any age will make a person more likely to encounter the ticks that spread Lyme disease. **(d)** The histograms have the same shapes, but females have a slightly lower incidence rate at every age. Females possibly spend less time outdoors in areas where they would encounter ticks.

1.11 Here is a stemplot for health expenditure per capita (in PPP). Data are rounded to units of hundreds. For example, Argentina's "1434" becomes 14. Stems are thousands, and are split, as prescribed. This distribution is right-skewed, with a single high outlier (United States). There seem to be two clusters of countries. The center of this distribution is around 20 ($2000 spent per capita), ignoring the outlier. The distribution varies from 0|1 (about $100 spent per capita) to 8|6 (about $8600 spent per capita).

```
0 | 1144
0 | 6679999
1 | 02344
1 | 7
2 | 2
2 | 9
3 | 0123
3 | 79
4 | 114
4 | 556
5 | 1
5 | 67
6 |
6 |
7 |
7 |
8 |
8 | 6
```

1.13 (a) the students.

1.15 (b) Square footage and average monthly gas bill are both quantitative variables.

1.17 (b) 58% to 61%.

1.19 (b) 80%. There are 50 observations, so the center would be between the 25th and 26th observations; both of these are 80%.

1.21 (b) 92%. The stems are rounded to whole percents; you cannot make finer judgments.

1.23 (a) Individuals are students who have finished medical school. **(b)** Five, in addition to "Name." "Age" (in years) and "USMLE" (score points) are quantitative. The others are categorical.

1.25 "Other colors" should account for 3%. A bar graph would be an appropriate display. If you included the "other" category, a pie chart could be made.

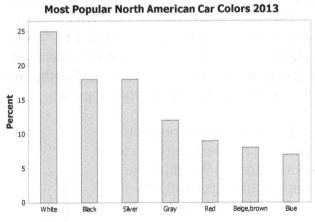

1.27 (a) A bar graph is given. **(b)** To make a pie chart, you would need to know the total number of deaths in this age group, or (equivalently), the number of deaths due to "other" causes.

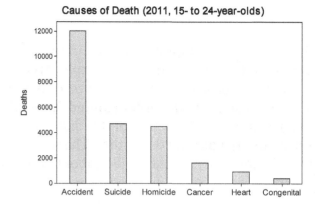

1.29 (a) A bar graph is provided. **(b)** A pie chart would be inappropriate, because these percentages aren't parts of one "whole"; each university's senior class is a "whole" in this situation.

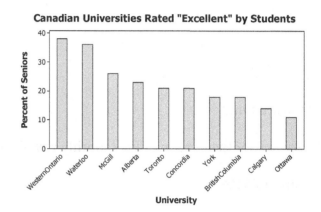

1.31 (a) Ignoring the four lower outliers, the distribution is roughly symmetric, is centered at a score of about 110, and has a range of 86 to 136. **(b)** 64 of the 78 scores are more than 100. This is 82.1%.

1.33 (1.) "Are you male or female?" is Histogram (c). There are two outcomes possible, and the difference in frequencies is likely to be smaller than the right-handed/left-handed difference in (2). **(2.)** "Are you right-handed or left-handed?" is Histogram (b), since there are more right-handed people than left handed people, and the difference is likely larger than the sex difference in (1). **(3.)** "What is your height in inches?" is Histogram (d). Height distribution is likely to be symmetric. **(4.)** "How many minutes do you study on a typical weeknight?" is Histogram (a). The variable takes on more than two values, and time spent studying may well be a right-skewed distribution, with most students spending less time studying, but some students studying a lot.

1.35 (a) States vary in population, so you would expect more nurses in California than in Wyoming, for example. Nurses per 100,000 provides a better measure of how many nurses are available to serve a state's population. **(b)** A histogram is provided. The District of Columbia, South Dakota, and

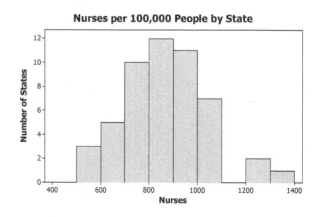

Massachusetts are the three states different from the others. Perhaps they could be considered outliers. The District of Columbia (Washington, D.C.) and Massachusetts are populous with large medical communities. It's difficult to know why South Dakota would also have an unusually high number of nurses for its population size.

1.37 The shape of the distribution is roughly symmetric (it might be called left skewed if we ignore the high outlier); with this scaling, 245 seems to be a high outlier. The center is about 171 (the 12th observation). The data range from about 94 to about 245.

```
 9  | 46
10  | 29
11  |
12  | 2
13  |
14  | 5
15  | 8
16  | 57
17  | 011399
18  | 22
19  | 2
20  | 1233
21  |
22  |
23  |
24  | 5
```

1.39 A time plot of seal pups. The decline in population is not seen in the stemplot made in Exercise 1.37.

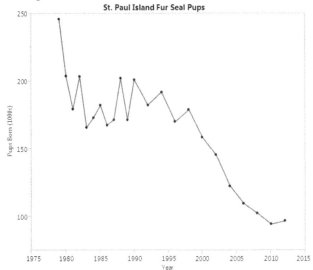

1.41 Coins with earlier (lower) dates are older, and rarer. There are more coins with larger dates (newer coins) than with smaller dates (older coins).

1.43 (a) Graph (a) appears to show the greatest increase. Vertical scaling can impact one's perception of the data. **(b)** In 2000, tuition was a bit more than $4000 and rises to almost $9000; this is an increase of almost $5000. Both plots describe the same data.

1.45 (a) A time plot of ozone hole size (area) is provided. There was a trend until about 1995; after that, we see only year-to-year variability. The hole has grown a lot over the period studied, but may have leveled out in recent years; the overall trend since about 2006 seems to be a decrease in size.

(b) A stemplot of ozone hole size (area) is provided. The midpoint is about 20 million of square kilometers.

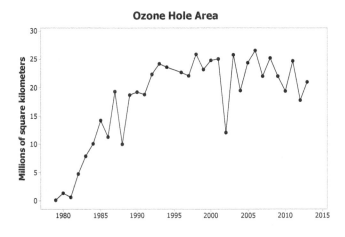

A stemplot fails to capture the relationship between size of hole and year.

```
0 | 0014
0 | 7
1 | 00124
1 | 7889999
2 | 122222334444
2 | 55556
```

1.47 is a Web-based exercise.

Chapter 2 – Describing Distributions with Numbers

2.1 Mean *e. Coli* level is $\bar{x} = \dfrac{291.0 + 10.9 + \ldots + 9.6}{16} = 56.28$ per milliliter. The mean is greater than most of the observations because of the two outliers (291.0 and 190.4).

2.3 The mean travel time is $\bar{x} = 31.25$ minutes. The median travel time is 22.5 minutes. The mean is significantly larger than the median due to the right skew in the distribution of times.

2.5 A histogram is given. Note the right skew. So, the mean is larger than the median. Here, the mean is 4.60566 and the median is 3.7034 tons per person.

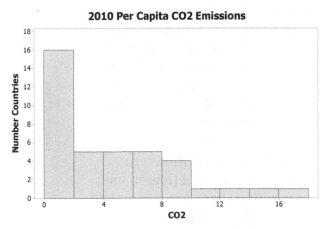

2.7 (a) Minimum = 11, Q_1 = 18, Median = 21, Q_3 = 26, Maximum = 51. **(b)** The boxplot shows right skew in the distribution of MPG values. There are several high outliers (which are most likely hybrid cars). Most software will identify the outliers automatically (if you do not want them identified, they are omitted from the graph).

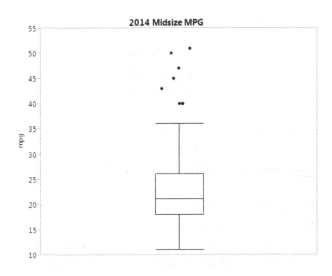

2.9 *IQR* = 26 – 18 = 8, so Q_3 + 1.5 × *IQR* = 26 + 1.5 × 8 = 38. There are eight values greater than 38 that would be identified as potential outliers (40, 40, 40, 43, 45, 47, 50, 51). Since Q_1 – 1.5 × *IQR* = 18 – 1.5 × 8 = 6, there are no potential outliers on the low end of the distribution.

2.11 Both data sets have the same mean and standard deviation (about 7.5 and 2.0, respectively). However, simple stemplots reveal that Data A has a very left-skewed distribution, while Data B has a slightly right-skewed distribution with a high outlier.

A		B
	1	3
7	4	
	5	257
1	6	58
2	7	079
7711	8	48
211	9	
	10	
	11	
	12	5

2.13 STATE: We'd like to know how logging impacts how many trees there are in 0.1 hectare plots in the rainforests of Borneo. PLAN: We'll create side-by-side boxplots for the three types of plots and compute appropriate summary statistics. SOLVE: According to the boxplots, none of the distributions are symmetric; Group 2 (logged one year earlier) has a low outlier and Group 3 (logged eight years earlier) is clearly left-skewed, while Group 1 (never logged) appears to be right-skewed. Because of the non-symmetric shapes, we will compute the five-number summaries for each.

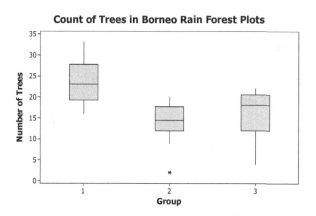

	Min	Q₁	M	Q₃	Max
Group 1 (never logged)	16	19.25	23	27.75	33
Group 2 (logged 1 year earlier)	2	12	14.5	17.75	20
Group 3 (logged 8 years earlier)	4	12	18	20.5	22

(If you compute the means and standard deviations, they are: Group 1: $\bar{x}$ = 23.75, s = 5.07; Group 2: $\bar{x}$ = 14.08, s = 4.98 and Group 3: $\bar{x}$ = 15.78, s = 5.76.) CONCLUDE: It is clear from the boxplots and summary statistics that plots that have never been logged have more trees than either type of logged plot. Further, if we compare the distributions and summary statistics for the two different types of logged plots, it takes a long time for the rainforest to recover from having been logged; while the centers of the distribution for plots logged 8 years earlier indicate more trees per plot on average, the distribution of the number of trees for plots logged 8 years earlier had more variability.

2.15 (b) 167.48

2.17 (b) 151.6, 163.5, 168.25, 174.3, 177.6

2.19 (a) 25%. Q_3 has 75% of observations equal to or less than its value.

2.21 (c) 8.2

2.23 (b) seconds

2.25 The distribution of incomes in this group is almost certainly right-skewed, so the mean is $62,597 and the median is $50,281.

2.27 With 849 colleges (an odd number), the median location is (849 + 1)/2 = 425, so the median is the 425th (ordered) endowment. The first quartile, Q_1, is found by taking the median of the first 424 endowments (when sorted). This would be the (424+1)/2 = 212.5th endowment. Similarly, Q_3 is found as the 637.5th endowment (212.5 endowments above the median).

2.29 The boxplots do not reveal the gap in the South between the rates for Georgia and the District of Columbia.

2.31 (a) A histogram of the survival times is given. The distribution is strongly right-skewed, with center around 100 days, and range from about 0 to about 600 days. **(b)** Because of the extreme right skew, we should use the five-number summary: 43, 82.5, 102.5, 151.5, 598 days. Notice that the median is closer to Q_1 than to Q_3.

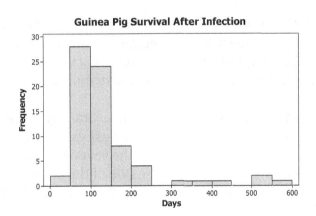

2.33 (a) Symmetric distributions are best summarized using $\bar{x}$ and s. The distribution for the treatment group was right skewed. The control distribution could be called rather symmetric, but it has a high outlier. **(b)** Removing the outliers reduces all three statistics (there is one less observation). However, the mean decreased by 8.45 seconds, which is about double the decrease in the median (3.5 seconds).

	With outlier	Without outlier
Mean	59.7	51.25
Standard deviation	63.0	50.97
Median	61	57.5

2.35 (a) The sixth observation must be placed at median for the original 5 observations. **(b)** No matter where you put the seventh observation, the median is one of the two repeated values above, because it will be the fourth (ordered) observation. The author's seventh point was the one at the extreme left.

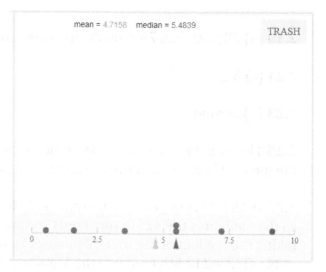

2.37 The mean for all 51 entries is 8.83%, far from the national percentage of 12.5%. You can't average averages. Some states, such as California and Florida, are larger and should carry more weight in the national percentage. Indeed, there are more people who are foreign-born living in Florida (about 3.65 million) than there are total residents in Wyoming (576,000).

2.39 Answers will vary, but a raise in the minimum wage will probably have a greater impact on the median income. Most Americans earn "middle income" or less; a few people earn huge amounts each year. The few large amounts will still pull the mean toward that end of the distribution.

2.41 Many answers are possible. Start by ensuring that the median is 12, by "locking" 12 as the fourth smallest value. We also have 4 specified as the minimum and 19 as the maximum, so the seven numbers must be 4, __, __, 12, __, __, 19. With three numbers either side of the median, the quartiles will be in positions 2 and 6. One set that works is 4, 7, 9, 12, 13, 14, 19.

2.43 (a) Weight losses that are negative correspond to weight *gains*. **(b)** A side-by-side boxplot (a version that reports suspected outliers using the 1.5 IQR rule) is provided. Gastric banding seems to produce higher weight losses, typically. Because both distributions are somewhat right-skewed (and there is a high outlier in the banding group), the five-number summary would be

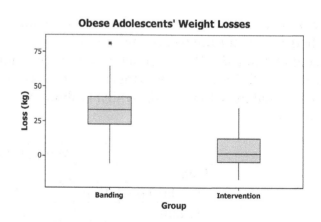

appropriate. The summary statistics are given below. **(c)** It's better to measure weight loss relative to initial weight. A loss of 5 kg would not mean the same if individuals started at different weights. Percent of excess weight lost would be a good measure. *Percent* reduction in BMI would also be good. **(d)** If the subjects that dropped out had continued, the difference between these groups would be as great or greater because many of the "lifestyle" dropouts had negative weight losses (i.e., weight gains), which would pull that group down.

	Min	Q₁	*M*	Q₃	Max
Banding	−5.40	22.70	33.35	42.67	81.40
Intervention	−17.00	−4.38	1.70	12.57	34.60

2.45 STATE: We'd like to describe the distribution of Wilshire 5000 stock index returns over the period from 1971 through 2013. PLAN: We'll graph the return with a histogram and a time plot. Based on what is seen there, we'll compute and report appropriate summary statistics. SOLVE: The histogram and summary statistics are given. CONCLUDE: The distribution of

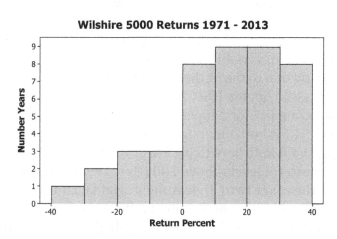

average returns is left-skewed. Most years, the average return is positive. Returns range from about −40% to about 40%, with the median return about 16%.

Mean	St. Dev.	Minimum	Q₁	Median	Q₃	Maximum
12.19	18.17	−37.23	0.98	16.06	26.77	37.38

2.47 STATE: We'd like to know how a "weather forecast" of good or bad weather for the following day will affect a waiter's tips, compared to no forecast. PLAN: create side-by-side boxplots of the three distributions, and compute appropriate summary statistics. SOLVE: Side-by-side boxplots of tip results are given. Good weather forecasts generally yielded better tips than the other two, and yielded

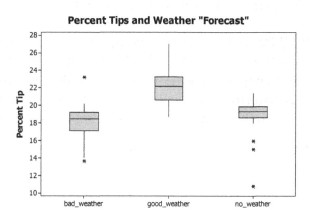

a relatively symmetric distribution. The bad weather forecast had an outlier on each end, while the no-weather message had three low outliers.

	Mean	St. Dev.	Minimum	Q₁	Median	Q₃	Maximum
Good weather	22.22	1.96	18.7	20.65	22.15	23.25	27.0
Bad weather	18.18	2.10	13.6	17.125	18.45	19.15	23.2
No weather	18.725	2.39	10.8	18.57	19.3	19.87	21.3

2.49 (a) With three age groups to compare and a large data set, we'll do side-by-side boxplots. All three distributions are right-skewed with high outliers. The median increases slightly with increasing age (from 173 to 190 to 204). We also see an increase in variability which is mostly due to the outliers as people age, although the IQRs are relatively the same (45 for people in their 20s and 51 for both older age groups).

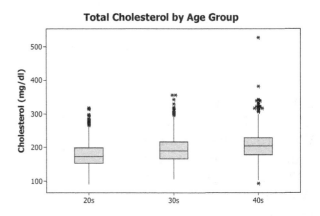

(b) We'll note here that 25% or more of the individuals in each age group had total cholesterol levels above 200 (Q_3 = 199 for the people in their 20's and 218 and 229 for the other two). Unless their original cholesterol levels were *extremely* high, the 4 or 24 people on medication in their 20s and 30s, respectively, probably wouldn't affect these distributions a great deal because there were roughly 950 people in each group (and these become small fractions of the total). However, there were 1139 people in their 40s; 117 of those on medication is more than 10% of this group. If those 117 had not been on medication, that distribution would likely show more variability and higher cholesterol readings (that might make the box longer, for example).

2.51 (a) Min = 1.3, Q_1 = 4.1, Median = 6.2, Q_3 = 13.4, Max = 27.1. (b) High end outliers will be values larger than 13.4 + 1.5 × (13.4 – 4.1) = 27.35. California, at 27.1% foreign-born is not an outlier.

2.53 Using Minitab, the five-number summary of cholesterol levels for people in their 20s is 92, 154, 173, 199, 318. We have IQR = 199 – 154 = 45. Outliers would be values smaller than 154 – 1.5 × 45 = 86.5 or larger than 199 + 1.5 ×45 = 266.5. Using this criterion, there are no low end outliers, but there are high end outliers (we saw these in the boxplots in the solution to Exercise 2.49).

2.55 is a Web-based exercise

Chapter 3 – The Normal Distributions

3.1 Sketches will vary. Use them to confirm that students understand the meaning of (a) symmetric and bimodal and (b) skewed to the left and unimodal.

3.3 μ = 2.5, which is the obvious balance point of the rectangle. The median is also 2.5 because the distribution is symmetric (so that median = mean), and half the area under the curve lies to the left and half to the right of 2.5.

3.5 Here is a sketch of the distribution of the Normal curve describing upper arm lengths of adult women. The tick marks are placed at the mean, and at one, two, and three standard deviations above and below the mean for scale.

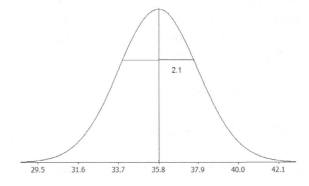

| 29.5 | 31.6 | 33.7 | 35.8 | 37.9 | 40.0 | 42.1 |

3.7 (a) In 95% of all years, monsoon rain levels are between 688 and 1016 mm—two standard deviations above and below the mean: 852 ± 2(82) = 688 to 1016 mm. **(b)** The driest 2.5% of monsoon rainfalls are less than 688 mm; this is more than two standard deviations below the mean.

3.9 We need to use the same scale, so recall that 6 feet = 72 inches. A woman 6 feet tall has standardized score $z = \dfrac{72 - 64.2}{2.8} = 2.79$ (quite tall, relatively). A man 6 feet tall has standardized score $z = \dfrac{72 - 69.4}{3.0} = 0.87$. Hence, a woman 6 feet tall is 2.79 standard deviations taller than average for women. A man 6 feet tall is only 0.87 standard deviations above average for men.

3.11 Let x be the monsoon rainfall in a given year. **(a)** $x \le 697$ mm corresponds to $z \le \dfrac{697 - 852}{82} = -1.89$, for which Table A gives 0.0294 = 2.94%. **(b)** 682 < x < 1022 corresponds to $\dfrac{682 - 852}{82} < z < \dfrac{1022 - 852}{82}$, or −2.07 < z < 2.07. This proportion is 0.9808 − 0.0192 = 0.9616 = 96.16%.

3.13 (a) We want the value such that the proportion below (to the left) is 0.65. Using Table A, looking for an area as close as possible to 0.6500, we find this value has $z = 0.39$ (software would give the more precise $z = 0.3853$). **(b)** Now we want the value such that the proportion above is 0.20. This means that we want a proportion of 0.80 below. Using Table A, looking for an area as close to 0.8000 as possible, we find this value has $z = 0.84$ (software gives $z = 0.8416$).

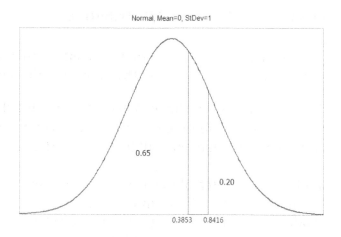

3.15 (c) Economic variables such as income and prices of houses are usually right-skewed.

3.17 (b) The curve is centered at 2.

3.19 (b) $266 \pm 2(16) = 234$ to 298 days.

3.21 (a) $z = \dfrac{132 - 100}{15} = 2.13$

3.23 (b) 0.1056

3.25 Sketches will vary, but should be some variation on the one shown here: the peak at 0 should be "tall and skinny," while near 1, the curve should be "short and fat."

3.27 70 is two standard deviations below the mean (that is, it has standard score $z = -2$), so about 2.5% (half of the outer 5%) of adults would have WAIS scores below 70.

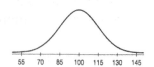

3.29 (a) We want the proportion less than z to be 0.30, so looking up a left-tail area of 0.3000 in the table, we find $z = -0.52$. (Software gives $z = -0.5244$.) **(b)** If 35% are more than z, then 65% are less than or equal to z. Hence, $z = 0.39$. (Software gives $z = 0.3853$.)

3.31 About 0.2119: The proportion of rainy days with rainfall pH below 5.0 is about 0.2119: $x < 5.0$ corresponds to $z < \dfrac{5.0 - 5.43}{0.54} = -0.80$, for which Table A gives 0.2119.

3.33 About 96.25%: For the $N(0.8750, 0.0012)$ distribution, $0.8725 < x < 0.8775$

corresponds to $\dfrac{0.8725 - 0.8750}{0.0012} < z < \dfrac{0.8775 - 0.8750}{0.0012}$, or $-2.08 < z < 2.08$, for which Table A gives $0.9812 - 0.0188 = 0.9624$.

For Exercises 3.35–3.37, let x denote the gas mileage of a randomly selected vehicle type from the population of 2014 model vehicles (excluding the high mileage outliers, as mentioned).

3.35 Cars with better mileage than the Beetle correspond to $x > 28$, which corresponds to $z > \dfrac{28 - 22.2}{5.2} = 1.12$. Hence, this proportion is $1 - 0.8686 = 0.1314$, or 13.14%.

3.37 The first and third quartiles have $z = -0.67$ and $z = 0.67$, respectively (use the symmetry of the Normal distribution to find one of these, for example, Q_1 with 0.2500 as the area to the left). Hence, the first quartile is $22.2 - (0.67)(5.2) = 18.72$ mpg, and the third quartile is $22.2 + (0.67)(5.2) = 25.68$ mpg.

3.39 (a) Larry's arm has $z = \dfrac{37.2 - 39.1}{2.3} = -0.83$. Using Table A, his percentile is 0.2033 (about the 20th percentile). **(b)** Answers will vary due to variation in students' arm lengths.

3.41 If x is the height of a randomly selected woman in this age group, we want the proportion corresponding to $x > 69.4$ inches. This corresponds to $z > \dfrac{69.4 - 64.2}{2.8} = 1.86$, which has proportion $1 - 0.9686 = 0.0314$, or 3.14%.

3.43 (a) Let X be a randomly selected man's SAT math score. $X > 750$ corresponds to $z > \dfrac{750 - 531}{121} = 1.81$. Hence, the proportion is $1 - 0.9649 = 0.0351$. **(b)** Let X be a randomly selected woman's SAT math score. $X > 750$ corresponds to $z > \dfrac{750 - 499}{112} = 2.24$. Hence, the proportion is $1 - 0.9875 = 0.0125$.

3.44 If the distribution is Normal, it must be symmetric about its mean—and in particular, the 10th and 90th percentiles must be equal distances below and above the mean—so the mean is 250 points. If 225 points below (above) the mean is the 10th (90th) percentile, this is 1.28 standard deviations below (above) the mean, so the distribution's standard deviation is $225/1.28 = 175.8$ points.

3.45 (a) About 0.6% of healthy young adults have osteoporosis (the cumulative probability below a standard score of −2.5 is 0.0062). **(b)** About 31% of this population of older women has osteoporosis: The BMD level that is 2.5 standard deviations below the young adult mean would standardize to −0.5 for these older women, and the cumulative probability for this standard score is 0.3085.

3.47 (a) 170,777/1,799,243 = 0.0949, or 9.49%. **(b)** There are 56,351 + 170,777 = 227,128 students with ACT score 28 or higher. This is 227,128/1,799,243 = 0.1262, or 12.62%. **(c)** If x is the ACT score, then $x > 28$ corresponds to $z > \dfrac{28 - 20.9}{5.4} = 1.31$, so the corresponding proportion is $1 - 0.9049 = 0.0951$, or 9.51%.

3.49 (a) A histogram is provided and appears to be roughly symmetric. **(b)** Mean = 543.2, Median = 540, Standard deviation = 61.69, Q1 = 500, Q3 = 580. The mean and median are close, and the distances of each quartile to the median are equal. These results are consistent with a Normal distribution. **(c)** If x is the score of a randomly selected GSU entering student, then we are assuming x has the $N(543.2, 61.69)$ distribution. The proportion of GSU students scoring higher than the

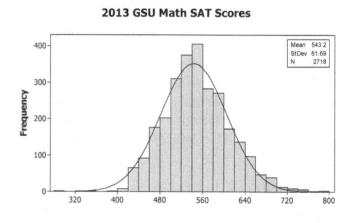

national average of 514 corresponds to the proportion of $x > 514$, or $z > \dfrac{514 - 543.2}{61.69} = -0.47$, or $1 - 0.3192 = 0.6808$, or 68.08%. **(d)** 859 of these students scored 510 or less, so 2718 – 859 = 1859 entering GSU students scored higher than 514, which represents 1859/2718 = 0.6840, or 68.4%. The nominal Normal probability in part (c) fits the actual data well.

3.51 (a) 14/548 = 0.0255 (2.55%) weighed less than 100 pounds. $x < 100$ corresponds to $z < \dfrac{100 - 161.58}{48.96} = -1.26$. Using Table A, the area to the left of –1.26 is 0.1038 (10.38%). **(b)** 33/548 = 0.0602 (6.02%) weighed more than 250 pounds. $x > 250$ corresponds to $z > \dfrac{250 - 161.58}{48.96} = 1.81$. Using Table A, about $1 - 0.9649 = 0.0351$ (3.51%) would be expected to weigh more than 250 pounds. **(c)** The Normal distribution model predicts 10.38% of women to weigh less than 100 pounds, while actually about 2.55% do. This is a substantial error since the Normal model also predicts 3.51% of values more than 250, where we actually observed 6.02% more than 250. In this application, the data seem to be far from Normal in distribution.

3.53 Because the quartiles of any distribution have 50% of observations between them, we seek to place the flags so that the reported area is 0.5. The closest the applet gets is an area of 0.4978, between –0.671 and 0.671. Thus the quartiles of any Normal distribution are about 0.67 standard deviations above and below the mean.

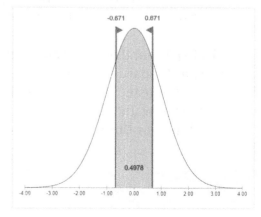

Note: *Table A places the quartiles at about 0.67; other statistical software gives ±0.6745.*

3.55 is a Web-based exercise.

Chapter 4 – Scatterplots and Correlation

4.1 (a) Explanatory: number of lectures attended; response: grade on final exam. **(b)** Explanatory: time exercising; response: calories burned. **(c)** Explanatory: time spent online using Facebook is explanatory; response: GPA (assuming that more time on Facebook means less time studying). **(d)** Explore the relationship.

4.3 For example: weight, sex, other food eaten by the students, type of beer (light, imported,...).

4.5 Outsource percent is the explanatory variable and should be on the horizontal axis. Delay percent is the response and should be on the vertical axis. These data do not support concerns of the critics.

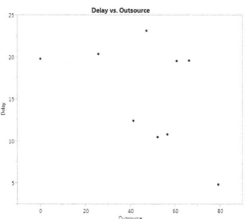

4.7 One could consider there to be two outliers; Frontier has an unusually low outsourcing percent and a high delay percent; Hawaiian has a very high outsourcing percent and a very low delay percent. Without Frontier, there would be a decreasing relationship that is approximately linear and moderately strong. Without Hawaiian, there is really no relationship, but two sets of points: five airlines with high delays, which don't seem to depend on outsourcing, and three airlines with low delay percentages that again don't seem to depend on outsourcing.

4.9 (a) Caution counties are marked with circles, the others with squares. **(b)** For both types of counties, there appears to be no relationship between homicide and suicide rates. The caution counties form a band in the lower portion of the graph, while the non-caution counties form a band in the upper portion.

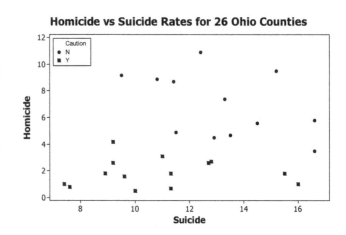

4.11 *r* would not change; units do not affect correlation.

4.13 In computing the correlation, note that $\bar{x}$ = 50 mph, s_x = 15.8114 mph, $\bar{y}$ = 26.8 mpg, and s_y = 2.6833 mpg. Refer to the table of standardized scores below, then note that $r = 0/4 = 0$. The correlation is zero because these variables do not have a straight-line relationship; the association is neither positive nor negative. Remember that correlation only measures the strength and direction of a *linear* relationship between two variables.

4.15 (c) The association should be negative (e.g., if slower reaction times mean less time to death).

4.17 (a) 0.9. Without the outlier, there is a strong positive linear relationship.

4.19 (c) A correlation close to 0 might arise from a scatterplot with no visible pattern, but there could be a nonlinear pattern. See Exercise 4.13, for example.

4.21 (a) 1. There would be a perfect, positive linear association. The line would be Exam2 = Exam1 − 10.

4.23 (b) Computation with calculator or software gives $r = 0.298$.

4.25 (a) Overall, there is a slightly negative association between these variables. **(b)** There is general disagreement—low BRFSS scores correspond to greater happiness, and these are associated with higher-ranked states (the least happy states, according to the objective measure). **(c)** It is hard to declare any of the data values as "outliers." It does not appear that any of the values are obviously outside of the general pattern. Perhaps one value (Rank = 8, BRFSS = 0.30) is an outlier, but this is hard to say.

4.27 (a) The scatterplot suggests a strong positive linear association between distance and time with respect to the spread of Ebola. **(b)** $r = 0.9623$. This is consistent with the pattern described in part (a). **(c)** Correlation would not change, since it does not depend on units.

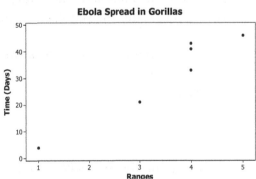

4.29 (a) The scatterplot is shown; note that neural activity is explanatory (and so should be on the horizontal axis). **(b)** The association is moderately strong, positive, and linear. The outlier is in the upper right corner (behavioral score is 155.2). **(c)** For all points, $r = 0.8486$.

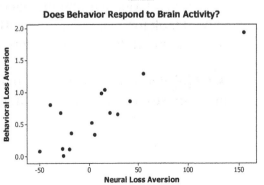

Without the outlier, $r = 0.7015$. The correlation is greater with the outlier because it fits the pattern of the other points; if one drew the line suggested by the other points, the outlier would extend the length of the line and would therefore decrease the relative scatter of the points about that line.

4.31 (a) The scatterplot is provided at right. **(b)** The plot suggests that there is a strong relationship between alcohol intake and relative risk of breast cancer (again, this is an observational study, so no causal relationship can be established here). It seems that type of alcohol has nothing to do with the increase since the same pattern and rate of increase is seen for both groups.

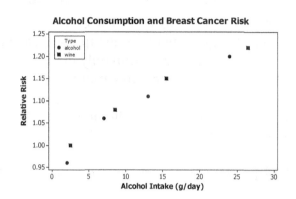

4.33 (a) The plot at right suggests that "Good" weather reports tend to yield higher tips. **(b)** The explanatory variable is categorical, not quantitative, so r cannot be used. Notice that we can arrange the categories any way, and these different arrangements would suggest different associations. Hence, it doesn't make sense to discuss a relationship direction here.

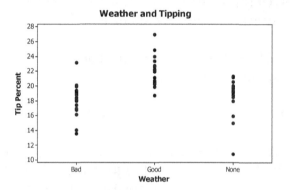

4.35 (a) The scatterplot is provided at right. Set B (the mad scientist's set) has stretched out the x-values, but the pattern is still the same.
(b) Units do not impact correlation. For both data sets, $r = 0.298$.

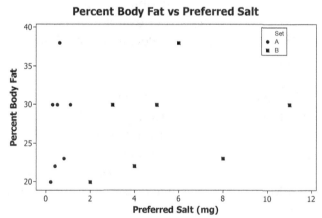

4.37 (a) Small-cap stocks have a lower correlation with municipal bonds, so the relationship is weaker. **(b)** She should look for a negative correlation (although this would also mean that this investment tends to *decrease* when bond prices rise).

4.39 (a) Because sex has a nominal scale, we cannot compute the correlation between sex and any other variable. There is a strong *association* between sex and income. Some writers and speakers use "correlation" as a synonym for "association," but this is not correct. **(b)** A correlation of $r = 1.09$ is impossible, because r is restricted to be between –1 and 1. **(c)** Correlation has no units, so "$r = 0.63$ centimeter" is incorrect.

4.41 (a) The correlation will be closer to 1. One possible answer is shown (see below, left). **(b)** Answers will vary, but the correlation will decrease, and can be made negative by dragging the point down far enough (see below, right).

4.43 PLAN: To investigate global warming, we'll create a scatterplot and look for an increasing (positive) pattern. SOLVE: The plot suggests that temperatures have been increasing overall, but there seems to have been a slowing in the past few years; this graph looks curved. Correlation may not be a useful measure here; $r = 0.6334$. CONCLUDE: Over time, average global temperatures have increased, but the increase may not be linear.

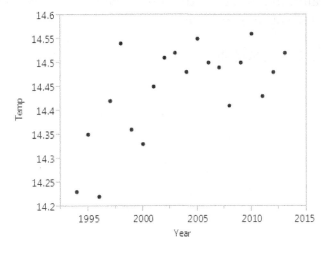

4.45 PLAN: To investigate the relationship between outside temperature and the percent of total heat loss due to beak, we plot heat loss from beak against outside temperature. We'll compute the correlation, if the relationship looks to be reasonably linear. SOLVE: The plot follows. Notice that there is a reasonably strong linear relationship. It seems reasonable to use

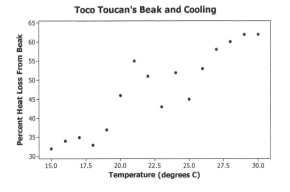

correlation to describe this relationship's strength and direction. In fact, $r = 0.9143$. CONCLUDE: When the outside temperature increases, a greater percentage of total heat loss is due to beak heat loss. That is, the beak plays a more important role in cooling down the toco toucan as the weather outside becomes hotter.

4.47 PLAN: We wish to explore the relationship pine cone supplies and squirrel density the following spring. We begin with a scatterplot, and compute the correlation if appropriate. SOLVE: A scatterplot shows a moderately strong, positive, linear association. The point at the upper right (5.3, 3.4) may be an outlier. This point seems to make the linear relationship appear more positive. Including the possible outlier, $r = 0.564$. If the outlier is omitted, $r = 0.4406$. CONCLUDE: The positive association supports the idea that squirrel populations increase when the pine cone supply is higher in the previous autumn. However, the relationship is somewhat weak; squirrels in the Yukon may have other good food sources.

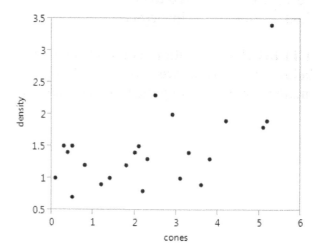

4.49 is a Web-based exercise.

Chapter 5 – Regression

5.1 (a) The slope is 1.033. On average, highway mileage increases by 1.033 mpg for each additional 1 mpg change in city mileage. **(b)** The intercept is 6.785 mpg. This is the highway mileage for a nonexistent car that gets 0 mpg in the city. Although this interpretation is valid, such a prediction would be invalid, since 0 is outside the range of the data (this is extrapolation, which will be addressed later in the chapter). **(c)** For a car that gets 16 mpg in the city, we predict highway mileage to be

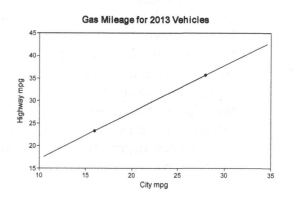

6.785 + (1.033)(16) = 23.31 mpg. For a car that gets 28 mpg in the city, we predict highway mileage to be 6.785 + (1.033)(28) = 35.71 mpg. **(d)** The regression line passes through all the points of prediction. The plot was created by drawing a line through the two points (16, 23.31) and (28, 35.71), corresponding to the city mileages and predicted highway mileages for the two cars described in (c).

5.3 (a) The slope is 1021. This means that for each year since 2000, forest loss averages about 1021 km^2. **(b)** If we measured in square meters, the slope would be 1021×10^6 = 1,021,000,000; a loss of 1 billion square meters per year (on average). In thousands of km^2, the slope would be 1.021; a loss of a bit more than 1000 km^2 per year (on average).

    Note: The point of this exercise is that units matter a great deal in regression. All these slopes represent the same relationship.

5.5 (a) The scatterplot (with the regression line) is shown. This relationship is certainly weak. **(b)** JMP output is shown. The regression equation is
$\widehat{Suicide}$ = 11.125 + 0.195(Homicide). **(c)** The slope means that for every suicide (per 100,000 people), there are about 0.195 homicides (per 100,000 people) in these Ohio counties. **(d)** We would predict 11.125 + 0.195(8.0) = 12.685 suicides.

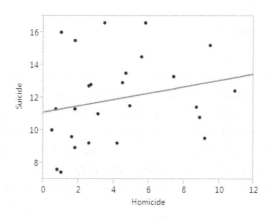

5.7 (a) The scatterplot is provided, with the regression line. Regression gives $\hat{y} = 1.0284 - 0.004498x$ (see Minitab output). The plot suggests a slightly curved pattern, not a strong linear pattern. A regression line is not useful for making predictions. **(b)** $r^2 = 0.031$. This confirms what we see in the graph: the regression line does a poor job summarizing the relationship between difference in begging intensity and growth rate. Only about 3% of the variation in growth rate is explained by the least-squares regression on difference in begging intensity.

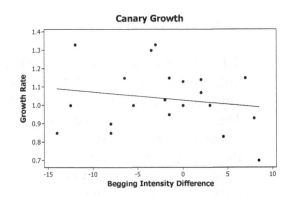

Minitab output

```
The regression equation is Growth = 1.028 - 0.0045 Difference

Predictor      Coef       Stdev      t-ratio      P
Constant    1.028409    0.039042     26.341    0.000
Difference  -0.004498   0.005808     -0.774    0.448

s = 0.1704   R-Sq = 3.1%
```

5.9 (a) Plot is provided following, left. **(b)** No; the pattern is curved, so linear regression is not appropriate for prediction. **(c)** For $x = 10$, we estimate $\hat{y} = 11.058 - 0.01466(10) = 10.91$, so the residual is $21.00 - 10.91 = 10.09$. The sum of the residuals is -0.01. **(d)** The first two and last four residuals are positive, and those in the middle are negative. Plot following, right.

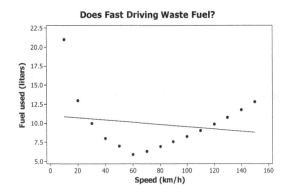

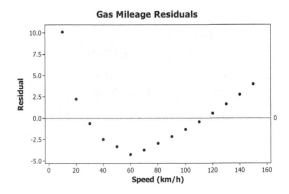

5.11 (a) Any point that falls exactly on the regression line will not increase the sum of squared vertical distances (which the regression line minimizes). Thus the regression line does not change. Possible output is shown, below left. Any other line (even if it passes through this new point) will necessarily have a higher total sum of squared prediction errors. The correlation changes (increases) because the new point reduces the relative scatter about the regression line. **(b)** Influential points are those whose *x*-coordinates are outliers. The regression line will "follow" an influential point if it is moved up or down in the *y* direction. An example is provided, below right.

5.13 (a) In the plot, Hawaiian Airlines is the point identified with "H." Since this point is an outlier and falls outside the *x* range of the other data points, it is influential, and will affect the regression line by "pulling" it. **(b)** With the outlier, *r* = −0.488. If the outlier is deleted from the data, *r* = −0.241. Notice that with the outlier, the correlation suggests a stronger linear relationship. **(c)** The two regression lines (one including the outlier, and the other without) are plotted. We see that the line based on the full data set (including the outlier) has been pulled down toward the outlier, indicating that the outlier is influential. Now, the regression line based on the complete (original) data set, including the outlier, is $\hat{y}$ = 21.815 − 0.12851*x*. Using this, when *x* = 79.1, we predict 11.65% delays. The other regression line (fit without the outlier), is $\hat{y}$ = 19.460 − 0.05528*x*, so our prediction would be 15.09% delays. The outlier impacts predictions because it impacts the regression line.

5.15 (a) The regression line is $\hat{y}$ = −44.831 + 0.1323 *x* (or, $\widehat{\text{Kills}}$ = −44.831 + 0.1323 Boats). **(b)** If 890,000 boats are registered, then by our scale, *x* = 890, and $\hat{y}$ = −44.831 + (0.1323)(890) = 72.92 manatees killed. The prediction seems reasonable, as long as conditions remain the same, because "890" is within the space of observed values of *x* on which the regression line was based. That is, this is not extrapolation. **(c)** If *x* = 0 (corresponding to no registered boats), then we would "predict" −44.831 manatees to be killed by boats. This is absurd, because it is clearly impossible for fewer than 0 manatees to be killed. This illustrates the folly of extrapolation... *x* = 0 is well outside the range of observed values of *x* on which the regression line was based.

5.17 Possible lurking variables include the IQ and socioeconomic status of the mother, as well as the mother's other habits (drinking, diet, etc.). These variables are associated with smoking in various ways, and are also predictive of a child's IQ. **Note:** *There may be an indirect cause-and-effect relationship at work here: some studies have found evidence that over time, smokers lose IQ points, perhaps due to brain damage caused by toxins from the smoke. So, perhaps smoking mothers gradually grow less smart and are less able to nurture their children's cognitive development.*

5.19 One example would be that men who are married, widowed, or divorced may be more "invested" in their careers than men who are single. There is still a feeling of societal pressure for a man to "provide" for his family.

5.21 (b) 0.2. Consider two points on the regression line—say (90,4) and (130,11). The slope of the line segment connecting these points is $\dfrac{11-4}{130-90}$ = 7/40 = 0.175.

5.23 (a) $y = 1000 + 100x$

5.25 (c) 16 cubic feet

5.27 (a) The slope of the line is positive.

5.29 (a) $\hat{y} = 24.2 + 6.0x$

5.31 (a) Since the slope is 3721.02, the least-squares regression line says that increasing the size of a diamond by 1 carat increases its price by 3721.02 Singapore dollars, on average. **(b)** A diamond of size 0 carats would have a predicted price of 259.63 Singapore dollars. This is probably an extrapolation, since the data set on which the line was constructed almost certainly had no rings with diamonds of size 0 carats. However, if the number is meaningful (dubious), then it refers to the cost of the gold content and other materials in the ring.

5.33 (a) The regression equation is $\hat{y} = 0.919 + 2.0647x$. For every degree Celsius, the toucan will lose about 2.06% more heat through its beak. **(b)** $\hat{y} = 0.919 + 2.0647(25) = 52.5$. At a temperature of 25 degrees Celsius, we predict a toucan to lose 52.5% more heat through its beak, on average. **(c)** Since R-Sq = 83.6%, 83.6% of the total variation in beak heat loss is explained by the straight-line relationship with temperature. **(c)** $r = \sqrt{r^2} = \sqrt{0.836} = 0.914$. Correlation is positive here, since the least-squares regression line has a positive slope.

5.35 (a) $b = r\, s_y / s_x = (0.5)\left(\dfrac{8}{40}\right) = 0.1$, and $a = \bar{y} - b\bar{x} = 75 - (0.1)(280) = 47$. The regression equation is $\hat{y} = 47 + 0.1x$. Each point of pre-exam total score means an additional 0.1 points on the final exam, on average. **(b)** Julie's pre-final exam total was 300, so we would predict a final exam score of $\hat{y} = 47 + (0.1)(300) = 77$. **(c)**

Julie is right; with a correlation of $r = 0.5$, $r^2 = (0.5)^2 = 0.25$, so the regression line accounts for only 25% of the variability in student final exam scores. That is, the regression line doesn't predict final exam scores very well. Julie's score could, indeed, be much higher or lower than the predicted 77. Since she is making this argument, one might guess that her score was, in fact, higher. Julie should visit the Dean.

5.37 (a) The regression equation is $\hat{y} = 28.037 + 0.521x$. $r = 0.555$. **(b)** The plot is provided. Based on Damien's height of 70 inches, we predict his sister Tonya to have height $\hat{y} = 28.037 + (0.521)(70) = 64.5$ inches (rounded). This prediction isn't expected to be very accurate because the correlation isn't very large; $r^2 = (0.555)^2 = 0.308$. The regression line explains only 30.8% of the variation in sister heights.

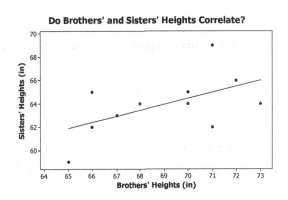

5.39 (a) The regression equation is $\hat{y} = 31.934 - 0.304x$. **(b)** The slope (–0.304) tells us that, on the average, for each additional 1% increase in returning birds, the number of new birds joining the colony decreases by 0.304. **(c)** When $x = 60$, we predict $\hat{y} = 13.69$ new birds will join the colony.

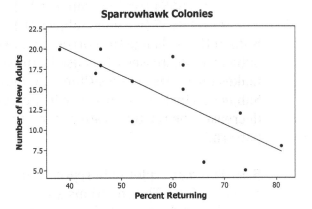

Minitab output

```
The regression equation is New = 31.93 - 0.3040PctRtn

Predictor  Coef     Stdev  t-ratio    p
Constant   31.934   4.838   6.60    0.000
PctRtn    -0.30402  0.0812 -3.74    0.003
s= 3.667   R-sq=56.0%    R-sq(adj)=52.0%
```

5.41 (a) The outlier is in the upper-right corner. **(b)** With the outlier omitted, the regression line is $\hat{y} = 0.586 + 0.00891x$. (This is the solid line in the plot.) **(c)** The line does not change much because the outlier fits the pattern of the other points; r changes because the scatter (relative to the line) is greater with the outlier removed, and the outlier is located consistently with the linear

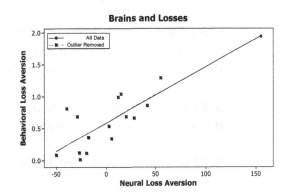

pattern of the rest of the points. **(d)** The correlation changes from 0.8486 (with all points) to 0.7015 (without the outlier). With all points included, the regression line is $\hat{y} = 0.585 + 0.0879x$ (nearly indistinguishable from the other regression line).

Minitab output – all points
```
The regression equation is Behave = 0.585 + 0.00879 Neural

Predictor    Coef    SE Coef    T      P
Constant   0.58496   0.07093   8.25  0.000
Neural    0.008794  0.001465   6.00  0.000
```
Minitab output – outlier removed
```
The regression equation is Behave = 0.586 + 0.00891 Neural

Predictor    Coef    SE Coef    T      P
Constant   0.58581   0.07506   7.80  0.000
Neural    0.008909  0.002510   3.55  0.004
```

5.43 (a) The two unusual observations are indicated on the scatterplot. **(b)** The correlations are

$r_1 = 0.4819$ (all observations)
$r_2 = 0.5684$ (without Subject 15)
$r_3 = 0.3837$ (without Subject 18)

Both outliers change the correlation. Removing Subject 15 decreases r because its presence makes the scatterplot less linear. Removing Subject 18 increases r because its presence decreases the relative scatter about the linear pattern.

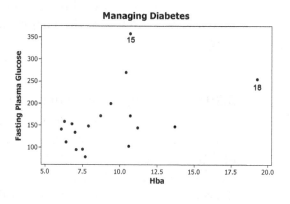

5.45 The scatterplot with regression lines added is given. The equations are

$\hat{y} = 66.4 + 10.4x$ (all observations)
$\hat{y} = 69.5 + 8.92x$ (without #15)
$\hat{y} = 52.3 + 12.1x$ (without #18)

While the equation changes in response to removing either subject, one could argue that neither one is particularly influential, because the line moves very little over the range of x (HbA) values. Subject 15 is an outlier in terms of its y-value; such points are typically not influential. Subject 18 is an outlier in terms of its x-value, but it is not particularly influential because it is consistent with the linear pattern suggested by the other points.

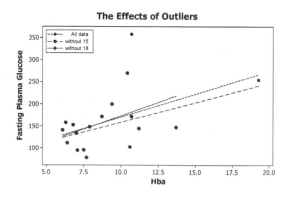

5.47 The correlation would be smaller. Individual weight will vary much more than the average weight for a given height.

5.49 Responses will vary. For example, students who choose the online course might have more self-motivation or have better computer skills (which might be helpful in doing well in the class; e.g., such students might do better at researching course topics on the Internet).

5.51 (a) For states where more than 40% take the SAT, we have

$\widehat{\text{MathSAT}} = 471.82 + 0.00048(\text{TeachSal})$. For these states, increasing the average teacher salary increases the mean Math SAT score by 0.00048 points, on average. **(b)** For states where less than 40% take the SAT, we have

$\widehat{\text{MathSAT}} = 472.8 + 0.0020(\text{TeachSal})$. For these states, increasing the average teacher salary increases the mean Math SAT score by 0.0020 points, on average. **(c)** The slopes here have opposite signs from that found in Exercise 5.50. This is an example of Simpson's paradox with continuous variables (although none of the relationships are particularly strong). Consideration of a third (lurking) variable changed the relationship.

The regression equation is			The regression equation is		
MathSAT = 472 + 0.000480			MathSAT = 473 + 0.00202		
Avg.tchrsal2013			Avg.tchrsal2013		
Predictor	Coef	SE Coef	Predictor	Coef	SE Coef
Constant	471.82	26.15	Constant	472.80	55.37
Avg.tchrsal2013	0.0004800	0.0004432	Avg.tchrsal2013	0.002022	0.001099
S = 20.2536	R-Sq = 4.7%		S = 28.7808	R-Sq = 12.8%	

5.53 Here is a (relatively) simple example to show how this can happen: suppose that most workers are currently 30 to 50 years old; of course, some are older or younger than that, but this age group dominates. Suppose further that each worker's current salary is his/her age (in thousands of dollars); for example, a 30-year-old worker is currently making $30,000. Over the next 10 years, all workers age, and their salaries increase. Suppose every worker's salary increases by between $4000 and $8000. Then every worker will be making *more* money than he/she did 10 years before, but *less* money than a worker of that same age 10 years before. During that time, a few workers will retire, and others will enter the workforce, but that large cluster that had been between the ages of 30 and 50 (now between 40 and 60) will bring up the overall median salary despite the changes in older and younger workers.

5.55 For a player who shot 80 in the first round, we predict a second-round score of $\hat{y} = 56.47 + (0.243)(80) = 75.91$. For a player who shot 70 in the first round, we predict a second-round score of $\hat{y} = 56.47 + (0.243)(70) = 73.48$. Notice that the player who shot 80 the first round (worse than average) is predicted to have a worse-than-average score the second round, but better than the first round. Similarly, the player who shot 70 the first round (better than average) is predicted to do better than average in the second round, but not as well (relatively) as in the first round. Both players are predicted to "regress" to the mean.

5.57 See Exercise 4.41 for the three sample scatterplots. A regression line is appropriate only for the scatterplot of part (b). For the graph in (c), the point not in the vertical stack is very influential—the stacked points alone give no indication of slope for the line (if indeed a line is an appropriate model). If the stacked points are scattered, we cannot place too much faith in the *y*-coordinate of the influential point; thus we cannot depend on the slope of the line, and so we cannot depend on predictions made with the regression line. The curved relationship exhibited by the scatterplot in (d) clearly indicates that predictions based on a straight line are not appropriate.

5.59 PLAN: We construct a scatterplot (with beaver stumps as the explanatory variable), and if appropriate, find the regression line and correlation. SOLVE: The scatterplot shows a positive linear association. Regression seems to be an appropriate way to summarize the relationship; the regression line is $\hat{y} =$ $-1.286+11.89x$. The straight-line relationship explains $r^2 =83.9\%$ of the variation in beetle larvae. CONCLUDE: The strong positive association supports the idea that beavers benefit beetles.

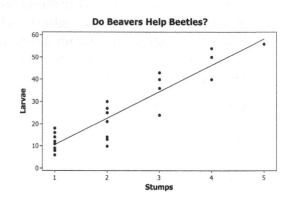

5.61 PLAN: We construct a scatterplot, with Forecast as the explanatory variable, and Actual as the response variable. If appropriate, we find the least-squares regression line. We consider the impact of the potential outlier (2005 season). SOLVE: The scatterplot shows a reasonable, but not very strong linear relationship between Forecast and Actual named storms. In recent years, it seems that there is no relationship between Forecast and Actual (a flat line). In the plot, the 2005 season is a noticeable outlier at the upper right. It is

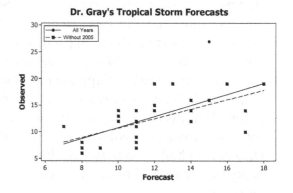

influential, pulling the regression line somewhat. We might consider deleting this point and fitting the line again. Deleting the point, we obtain the solid regression line, $\hat{y} = 2.753 + 0.7964$ Forecast when the original equation was $\hat{y} = 1.668 + 0.920$ Forecast. If the forecasts were perfect, the intercept of this line would be 0, and the slope would be 1, for reference. Deleting the 2005 season, $r = 0.628$, and $r^2 = 39.4\%$. Even after deleting the outlier, the regression line explains only 39.4% of variation in number of hurricanes. CONCLUDE: Predictions using the regression line are not very accurate. However, there is a positive association... so a forecast of many hurricanes may reasonably be expected to forebode a heavy season for hurricanes.

5.63 PLAN: We plot marathon times by year for each sex, using different symbols. If appropriate, we fit least-squares regression lines for predicting time from year for each gender. We then use these lines to guess when the times will concur. SOLVE: The scatterplot is provided below, with regression lines plotted. The regression lines are:

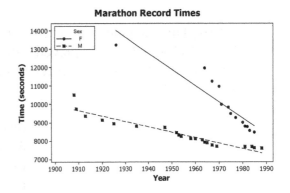

For men: $\hat{y} = 66{,}072 - 29.535x$

For women: $\hat{y} = 182{,}976.15 - 87.73x$

Although the lines appear to fit the data reasonably well (and the regression line for women would fit better if we omitted the outlier associated with year 1926), this analysis is inviting you to extrapolate, which is never advisable. CONCLUDE: Using the regression lines plotted, we might expect women to "outrun" men by the year 2009. Omitting the outlier, the line for women would decrease more steeply, and the intersection would occur sooner, by 1995. We'll note that as of 2014, this prediction has not happened.

5.65 and **5.67** are Web-based exercises.

Chapter 6 – Two-Way Tables

6.1 (a) This table describes 736 + 450 + 193 + 205 + 144 + 80 = 1808 people, and 736 + 450 + 193 = 1379 played video games. **(b)** (736 + 205)/1808 = 0.5205 = 52.05%. We do this for all three grade levels. The complete marginal distribution for grades is

Grade	Percent
As and Bs	52.05%
Cs	32.85%
Ds and Fs	15.10%

Of all boys, 32.85% + 15.10% = 47.95% received a grade of C or lower.

6.3 There are 736 + 450 + 193 = 1379 players. Of these, 736/1379 = 53.37% earned As or Bs. Similarly, there are 205 + 144 + 80 = 429 nonplayers. Of these, 205/429 = 47.79% earned A's or B's. Continuing, the conditional distributions of grades follow:

Grades	Players	Nonplayers
As and Bs	53.37%	47.79%
Cs	32.63%	33.57%
Ds and Fs	14.00%	18.65%

If anything, players have slightly higher grades than nonplayers, but this could be due to chance.

6.5 Two examples are shown. In general, choose a to be any number from 10 to 50, and then all the other entries can be determined.

30	20
30	20

50	0
10	40

6.7 (a) For Rotorua district, 79/8889 = 0.0089, or 0.9%, of Maori are in the jury pool, while 258/24,009 = 0.0107, or 1.07%, of the non-Maori are in the jury pool. For Nelson district, the corresponding percents are 0.08% for Maori and 0.17% for non-Maori. Hence, in each district, the percent of non-Maori in the jury pool exceeds the percent of Maori in the jury pool. **(b)** Combining the regions into one table:

	Maori	Non-Maori
In jury pool	80	314
Not in jury pool	10,138	56,353
Total	10,218	56,667

For the Maori, the overall percent in the jury pool is 80/10,218 = 0.0078, or 0.78%, while for the non-Maori, the overall percent in the jury pool is 314/56,667 = 0.0055, or 0.55%. Hence, overall the Maori have a larger percent in the jury pool, but in each region they have a lower percent in the jury pool. **(c)** The reason for Simpson's paradox occurring with this example is that the Maori constitute a large proportion of Rotorua's population, while in Nelson they are a small minority community.

6.9 (b) 150 teens in schools that forbid cell phones

6.11 (a) the marginal distribution of school permissiveness

6.13 (c) the conditional distribution of the frequency that a teen brings a cell phone to school among the schools that forbid cell phones

6.15 (b) the conditional distribution of school permissiveness among those who brought their cell phones to school every day

6.17 (b) an example of Simpson's paradox

6.19 For each type of injury (accidental, not accidental), the distribution of ages is produced below.

	Accidental	Not accidental
8–13	19.0%	4.0%
14–18	42.2%	35.8%
19–22	15.4%	20.8%
23–30	23.4%	39.4%

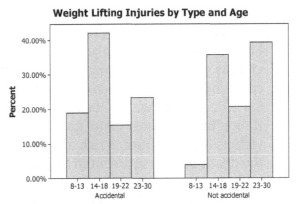

We see that among accidental weight-lifting injuries, the percentage of relatively younger lifters is larger, while among the injuries that are not accidental, the percentage of relatively older lifters is larger.

6.21 The percent of single men with no income is 513/4938 = 0.1039, or 10.39%. The percent of men with no income who are single is 513/1918 = 0.2675, or 26.75%.

6.23 (a) We need to compute percents to account for the fact that the study included many more married men than single men, so we would expect their numbers to be higher in every job grade (even if marital status had no relationship with income). **(b)** A table of percents is provided; descriptions of the relationship may vary. Single and widowed men had higher percents of no income; single men had the lowest (and widowed men the highest) percents of incomes over $100,000.

	Single	Married	Divorced	Widowed
No income	26.75%	51.87%	20.07%	1.30%
$100,000 and up	4.76%	85.43%	8.99%	0.81%

6.25 (a) The two-way table of race (White, Black) versus death penalty (Death penalty, No death penalty) follows:

	White defendant	Black defendant
Death penalty	19	17
No death penalty	141	149

(b) For black victims: The percentage of white defendants given the death penalty is $0/9 = 0$, or 0%. The percentage of black defendants given the death penalty is $6/103 = 0.058$, or 5.8%. For white victims: The percentage of white defendants given the death penalty is $19/151 = 0.126$, or 12.6%. The percentage of black defendants given the death penalty is $11/63 = 0.175$, or 17.5%. Hence, for both victim races, black defendants are given the death penalty relatively more often than white defendants. However, overall, referring to the table in (a), $19/160 = 0.119$, or 11.9%, of white defendants got the death penalty, while $17/166 = 0.102$, or 10.2%, of black defendants got the death penalty. This illustrates Simpson's paradox. **(c)** For white defendants, $(19 + 132)/(19 + 132 + 0 + 9) = 0.9438 = 94.4\%$ of victims were white. For black defendants, only $(11 + 52)/(11 + 52 + 6 + 97) = 0.3795$, or 37.95%, of victims were white. Meanwhile, the death penalty was predominantly assigned to cases involving white victims: 14.0% of all cases with a white victim, while only 5.5% of all cases with a black victim had a death penalty assigned to the defendant. Hence, because most white defendants' victims are white, and cases with white victims carry additional risk of a death penalty, white defendants are being assigned the death penalty more often overall.

6.27 PLAN: From the given two-way table of results, find and compare the conditional distributions of outcome (success, no success) for each treatment (Chantix, Bupropion, and Placebo). **SOLVE:** The percentages for each column are provided in the table. For example, for Chantix, the percentage of successes (no smoking in weeks 9–12) is $155/(155 + 197) = 0.4403$, or 44.0%. Because we're comparing success rates, we'll leave off the row for those who smoked in weeks 9–12, as this is just 100—the percent who did not smoke in weeks 9–12.

	Chantix	Bupropion	Placebo
Percent not smoking in weeks 9–12	44.0%	29.5%	17.7%

CONCLUDE: Clearly, a larger percent of subjects using Chantix were not smoking during weeks 9–12, compared with results for either of the other treatments. In fact, as we'll learn later, this result is statistically significant ... random chance doesn't easily explain this difference, and we might conclude that Chantix use increases the chance of success.

6.29 PLAN: Calculate and compare the conditional distributions of sex for each degree level. SOLVE: We compute, for example, the percentage of women earning associate's degrees: $646/(646 + 383) = 0.6278$, or 62.78%. The table shows the percent of women at each degree level, which is all we need for comparison. CONCLUDE: Women constitute a substantial majority of associate's, bachelor's, and master's degrees, and a small majority of doctor's and professional degrees.

Degree	Female
Associate's	62.78%
Bachelor's	57.88%
Master's	61.94%
Professional or Doctor's	53.53%

6.31 PLAN: Find and compare the conditional distributions for health (self-reported) for each group (smokers and nonsmokers). SOLVE: The table provides the percent of subjects with various health outlooks for each group. CONCLUDE: Clearly, the outlooks of current smokers are generally bleaker than those of current nonsmokers. Much larger percentages of nonsmokers reported being in "excellent" or "very good" health, while much larger percentages of smokers reported being in "fair" or "poor" health.

	Health outlook				
	Excellent	Very good	Good	Fair	Poor
Current smoker	6.2%	28.5%	35.9%	22.3%	7.2%
Current nonsmoker	12.4%	39.9%	33.5%	14.0%	0.3%

6.33 Because the numbers of students who use (or do not use) medications are different, we find the conditional distributions of those who do and do not use medications. Those who use medications are less likely to have optimal sleep quality and more likely to have poor sleep quality than those who do not use medications. This is certainly a case where one would not want to ascribe causation: Do those who use medications to stay awake have poor sleep quality because they use the medication, or do they use the medications to stay awake because they had poor sleep quality before using them?

	Sleep quality		
	Optimal	Borderline	Poor
Use medications	21.3%	30.5%	48.3%
Do not use medications	38.2%	26.7%	35.2%

6.35 is a Web-based exercise.

Chapter 7 – Exploring Data: Part I Review

Test Yourself Exercise Answers are sketches. All of these problems are similar to ones found in Chapters 1–5, for which the solutions in this manual provide more detail.

7.1 (c)

7.3 (d)

7.5 (c)

7.7 (c)

7.9 (c)

7.11 (a) centimeters; **(b)** centimeters; **(c)** centimeters; **(d)** grams^2

7.13 (d) 43 of 51 observations are at least 20

7.15 (c) About 54% use a search engine at least once a day; an additional 15–16% use one at least three times per week.

7.17 (a) 99.7% of all values are within 3σ of μ in a Normal distribution; this becomes $0.800 - 3(0.078) = 0.566$ to $0.800 + 3(0.078) = 1.034$ mm. **(b)** 0.878 is 1 standard deviation above the mean; about 16% (15.87%) will have thorax lengths longer than 0.878 mm.

7.19 (a) Minimum = 7.2, Q_1 = 8.5, M = 9.3, Q_3 = 10.9, Maximum = 12.8 **(b)** M = 27 **(c)** 25% of values exceed Q_3 = 30 **(d)** Yes. Virtually all Torrey pine needles are longer than virtually all Aleppo pine needles. There is no overlap in the distributions, as seen by comparing, say, the minimum for Torrey pine needles (about 21) to the maximum for Aleppo pine needles (12.8).

7.21 (a)

7.23 (c)

7.25 (d)

7.27 (d)

7.29 (d)

7.31 (c)

7.33 (a)

7.35 (a) No **(b)** r^2 = 0.64, or 64%

7.37 (a) 8.683 kg **(b)** 10.517 kg
(c) Such a comparison would be
unreasonable because the lean group is
less massive and, therefore, would be
expected to burn less energy on
average. **(d)** See scatterplot. **(e)** Based
on the plot, it appears that the rate of
increase in energy burned per kilogram
of mass is about the same for both
groups. The obese monkeys burn less
energy than the lean monkeys, because

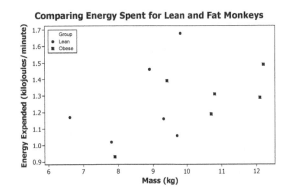

their points tend to be below the others. Do they expend less energy because they
are obese, or are they obese because they expend less energy?

7.39 (a) 190/8474 = 0.0224, or 2.24% **(b)** 633/8474 = 0.0747, or 7.47%
(c) 27/633 = 0.0427, or 4.27% **(d)** 4621/8284 = 0.5578, or 55.78% **(e)** The
conditional distribution of CHD for each level of anger is tabulated below. The result
for the high anger group was computed in part (c), for example. Clearly, angrier
people are at greater risk of CHD.

Low anger	Moderate anger	High anger
1.70%	2.33%	4.27%

7.41 The time plot shows a lot of fluctuation
from year to year, but also shows a recent
increase: Before 1972, the discharge rarely
rose above 600 km³, but since then, it has
exceeded that level more than half the time. A
histogram or stemplot cannot show this
change over time.

7.43 (a) The plot is provided. **(b)** The least-squares regression line is
$\hat{y} = 144.79 - 0.0659x$. The slope is negative, suggesting that the ice breakup day is
decreasing (by 0.0659 days per year) **(c)** The regression line is not very useful for
prediction, as it accounts for only about 9% ($r^2 = 0.0903$) of the variation in ice
breakup time.

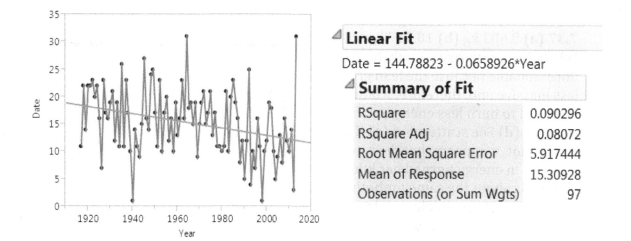

2012 Teacher's Salaries around the World

7.45 (a) A histogram is provided. **(b)** Luxembourg is the outlier, with an average starting salary of $65,171. Without that observation, the distribution is fairly symmetric. **(c)** The mean and standard deviation are $\bar{x}$ = $27,381.4 and s = $9651.78. Some students may instead report the five-number summary, which is Min = $9,526, Q_1 = $23,130, M = $28,328, Q_3 = $32,629, Max = $46,456. **(d)** The U.S. average starting salary ($36,858) is above the third quartile. Only six countries (including Luxembourg) pay their teachers a higher starting salary.

7.47 STATE: How does angle of deformity vary among young HAV patients requiring surgery? PLAN: Display the distribution with a graph, and compute appropriate numerical summaries. SOLVE: A stemplot is shown; a histogram could also be used. The distribution seems to be fairly Normal, apart from a high outlier of 50°. The five-number summary is preferred because of the outlier: Min = 13°, Q_1 = 20°, M = 25°, Q_3 = 30°, Max = 50°. (The mean and standard deviation are $\bar{x}$ = 25.4211° and s = 7.4748°.) CONCLUDE: Student descriptions of the distribution will vary. Most patients have a deformity angle in the range of 15° to 35°.

1	34
1	66788
2	000111123
2	55556666888
3	00012224
3	88
4	
4	
5	0

7.49 STATE: Can severity of MA be used to predict severity of HAV? PLAN: We examine the relationship with a scatterplot and (if appropriate) a correlation and regression line. SOLVE: MA angle is the explanatory variable, so it should be on the horizontal axis of the scatterplot. The scatterplot shows a moderate to weak positive linear association, with one clear outlier (the patient with HAV angle 50°). The correlation is $r = 0.302$, and the regression line is $\hat{y} = 19.723 + 0.3388x$. CONCLUDE: MA angle can be used to give (very rough, imprecise) estimates of HAV angle, but the spread is so wide that the estimates would not be very reliable. The linear relationship explains only $r^2 = 9.1\%$ of the variation in HAV angle.

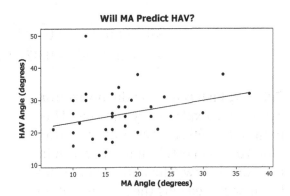

7.51 STATE: How does the cylinder wall thickness influence the gate velocity chosen by the skilled workers? PLAN: We will examine the relationship with a scatterplot and (if appropriate) a correlation and regression line. SOLVE: The scatterplot, shown with the regression line $\hat{y} = 70.44 + 274.78x$, shows a moderate, positive linear relationship. The linear relationship explains about $r^2 = 49.3\%$ of the

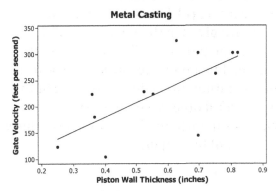

variation in gate velocity. CONCLUDE: The regression formula might be used as a rule of thumb for new workers to follow, but the wide spread in the scatterplot suggests that there may be other factors that should be taken into account in choosing the gate velocity.

7.53 (a) The scatterplot of 2003 returns against 2002 returns shows (ignoring the outlier) a strong negative association. **(b)** The correlation for all 23 points is $r = -0.616$; with the outlier removed, $r = -0.838$. The outlier deviates from the linear pattern of the other points; removing it makes the negative association stronger, and so r moves closer

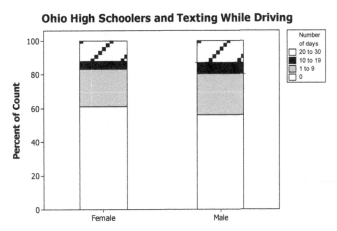

to -1. **(c)** Regression formulas are given in the table. The first line is solid in the plot; the second is the dashed line. The least-squares regression line makes the sum of the squares of the vertical deviations of the points from the line as small as possible. The line for the 22 other funds is so far below Fidelity Gold that the squared deviation is very large. The line must pivot up toward Fidelity Gold in order to minimize the sum of squares for all 23 deviations. Fidelity Gold is very influential.

	r	Equation
All 23 funds	−0.6230	$\hat{y} = 29.2512 - 0.4501x$
Without Gold	−0.8722	$\hat{y} = 18.1106 - 0.9429x$

7.55 (a) Fish catch (on the horizontal axis) is the explanatory variable. The point for 1999 is at the bottom of the plot. **(b)** The correlations are given in the table below. The outlier decreases r because it weakens the strength of the association. **(c)** The two regression lines are given in the table; the solid line in the plot uses all points, while the dashed line omits the outlier. The effect of the outlier on the line is small: There are several other years with similar changes in bushmeat biomass. Also, this year was not particularly extreme in the amount of fish caught.

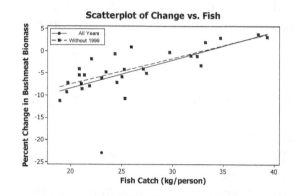

	r	Equation
All points	0.672	$\hat{y} = -21.09 + 0.6345x$
Without 1999	0.804	$\hat{y} = -19.05 + 0.5788x$

Chapter 8 – Producing Data: Sampling

8.1 (a) The population is (all) college students. (Even though the political scientist only obtained a list of all 3456 undergraduates at her college, she wanted to know about all college students.) **(b)** The sample is the 104 students at the researcher's college who returned the questionnaire. Because she only has her own college to sample from, the population she can make conclusions about is students at her college.

8.3 (a) The population is all users of the software. Unless the company's market is primarily educational, the 1100 individuals (who are mostly faculty) will not represent the population. **(b)** The sample is the 186 people who completed the survey.

8.5 Because all the students surveyed are enrolled in a special senior honors class, these students may be more likely to be interested in joining the club (and more willing to pay $35 to do so). The direction of bias is likely to overestimate the proportion of all psychology majors willing to pay to join this club. This is a convenience sample.

8.7 Number from 01 to 26 alphabetically (down the columns). With the applet: Population = 1 to <u>26</u>, select a sample of size <u>5</u>, then click <u>Reset</u> and <u>Sample</u>. With Table B, enter at line 141 and choose 23 = Rodriguez, 12 = Gemayel, 16 = Ippolito, 25 = Sgambellone, and 02 = Ahmadiani.

8.9 With the election close at hand, the polling organization wants to increase the accuracy of its results. Larger samples provide better information about the population.

8.11 Label the suburban townships from 01 to 30 alphabetically (down the columns). With Table B, enter at line 116 and choose 14 = New Trier, 03 = Bloom, 10 = Lemont, 22 = Proviso, and 06 = Cicero. Next, label the Chicago townships from 1 to 8, down the columns. With Table B, enter at line 126 and choose 6 = Rogers Park, 2 = Jefferson, and 7 = South Chicago.

8.13 (a) The population is all physicians practicing in the United States. The sample size is $n = 2379$. If the 2379 were randomly selected, we could draw conclusions, but there was too much nonresponse. **(b)** The nonresponse rate is $\dfrac{100,000 - 2379}{100,000} = 97.62\%$. We don't know the attitudes of the nonrespondents about health care reform, so the results may not be credible. **(c)** They only received 2379 responses.

8.15 (a) The sample was not randomly selected. **(b)** The true percentage is most likely lower. People who don't listen often probably don't visit the NPR Facebook page.

8.17 (a) all customers who have purchased something in the last year

8.19 (b) 5458, 0815, 0727, 1025, 6027

8.21 (b) a stratified random sample (plots are stratified by terrain)

8.23 (c) 04, 18, 07, 13, 02, 05. (Notice that in part (b), "07" appears in the sample twice. Option (a) includes numbers not in the 01 to 30 range.)

8.25 (b) The result for the entire sample is more accurate because it comes from a larger sample (people over 65 are a subset of the original sample).

8.27 The population is the 1000 envelopes stuffed during a given hour. The sample is the 40 envelopes selected.

8.29 With the applet: Population = 1 to <u>287</u>, select a sample of size <u>20</u>, then click <u>Reset</u> and <u>Sample</u>. Using Table B, number the area codes 001 to 287. Then, enter at line 122, and pay attention to the instructions that if we use the table, we'll pick only five numbers. The selected area codes are 138, 159, 052, 087, and 275.

8.31 The questions were worded very differently. The U.S. has the Second Amendment that allows guns (and a very active National Rifle Association that supports gun ownership). Canada has very different gun laws; gun ownership is generally forbidden. Given these facts, opinions would differ in any case (even if the questions were worded the same).

8.33 Online polls, call-in polls, and voluntary response polls in general tend to attract responses from those who have strong opinions on the subject and, therefore, are often not representative of the population as a whole. On the other hand, there is no reason to believe that randomly chosen adults would overrepresent any particular group; so the responses from such a group give a more reliable picture of public opinion.

8.35 (a) Assign labels 0001 through 5024, enter the table at line 114, and select: 4514, 0381, 0202, 0915, and 1776. **(b)** More than 171 respondents have run red lights. We would not expect very many people to claim they *have* run red lights when they have not, but some people will deny running red lights when they have.

8.37 (a) Each person has a 10% chance: 4 of 40 men, and 3 of 30 women. **(b)** This is not an SRS because not every group of 7 people can be chosen; the only possible samples are those with 4 men and 3 women.

8.39 (a) How the sample was obtained can contribute to bias in the results, if the sampling is not done randomly and fairly. We need to try to avoid undercoverage, for example. **(b)** Answers will vary. For example, exactly how the 655 Internet users were selected is not given.

8.41 Sample separately in each stratum; that is, assign separate labels, then choose the first sample, then continue on in the table to choose the next sample, etc. Beginning with line 112 in Table B, we choose:

Forest type	Labels	Parcels selected
Climax 1	01 to 36	04, 11, 19, 35
Climax 2	01 to 72	27, 30, 57, 62, 56, 02, 06
Climax 3	01 to 31	08, 02, 25
Secondary	01 to 42	11, 17, 14, 29

8.43 (a) Since 200/5 = 40, we will choose one of the first 40 names at random. Beginning on line 120, the addresses selected are 35, 75, 115, 155, and 195. (Only the first number is chosen from the table.) **(b)** All addresses are equally likely; each has chance 1/40 of being selected. To see this, note that each of the first 40 addresses has chance 1/40 because one is chosen at random. But each address in the second 40 is chosen exactly when the corresponding address in the first 40 is chosen, so each of the second 40 also has chance 1/40. And so on. This is not an SRS because the only possible samples have exactly 1 address from the first 40, one address from the second 40, and so on. An SRS could contain any five of the 200 addresses in the population. Note that this view of systematic sampling assumes that the number in the population is a multiple of the sample size.

8.45 (a) This design would omit households without telephones, those with only cell phones, and those with unlisted numbers. Such households would likely be made up of poor individuals (who cannot afford a phone), those who choose not to have landline phones, and those who do not wish to have their phone numbers published. **(b)** Those with unlisted landline numbers would be included in the sampling frame when a random-digit dialer (RDD) is used. (Additionally, RDDs exclude cell phones, although students may not be aware of this fact. For a discussion of this issue, see http://www.mysterypollster.com/main/2004/10/arianna_huffing.html).

8.47 (a) The wording is clear, but will almost certainly be slanted toward a high positive response. (Would anyone hear the phrase "skyrocketing gas prices" and *not* be inclined to agree that drilling for oil in Alaska is a good idea?) **(b)** The wording is clear, and it makes the case for a national health care system, and so will slant responses toward "yes." (**Note:** Some students will say that making a case for a national health care system will slant the responses toward "no.") **(c)** This survey question is most likely to produce a response similar to: "Uhh … yes? I mean, no? I'm sorry, could you repeat the question?" (And, if the person is able to understand the question, it is slanted in favor of day care subsidies.)

8.49 In Canada, as in many places, elected officials aren't necessarily qualified to make decisions about statistics. In this case, the minister is terribly misguided. Critics of the proposal are worried that the sample will not be representative of the population—presumably because people who fill out the optional long-form questions will be systematically different from those who don't. Larger samples do not address such problems of bias.

8.51 is a Web-based exercise.

Chapter 9 – Producing Data: Experiments

9.1 (a) The explanatory variable is the amount of alcohol drunk. The response is heart disease (unclear how this was measured). **(b)** Weight, sleep, exercise, etc., would be considered to be lurking variables, as they are not either the primary explanatory or response variables. (Some of these would be considered to be confounding because, for example, good exercise habits should promote heart health.) **(c)** Without an experiment, no causal relationship can be made.

9.3 This is an observational study, so it is not reasonable to conclude any cause-and-effect relationship. At best, we might advise smokers that they should be mindful of potential weight gain after smoking cessation and its accompanying ailments.

9.5 Subjects: the students. Factors: type of attack and prime used. Treatments: for the prime: *love thy neighbor* prime or *eye-for-an-eye* prime; for the type of attack: on military target or on cultural/educational target. Response variable: rating of U.S. reaction to attack.

		Prime used	
		Love-thy-neighbor	Eye-for-an-eye
Target	Military	1	2
	Cultural	3	4

9.7 Making a comparison between the treatment group and the percent finding work *last year* is not helpful. Over a year, many things can change: the state of the economy, hiring costs (due to an increasing minimum wage or the cost of employee benefits), etc. (In order to draw conclusions, we would need to make the $500 bonus offer to some people and not to others during the same time period, and compare the two groups.)

9.9 (a) Diagram below. **(b)** If using Table B, label 01 to 36 and take two digits at a time.

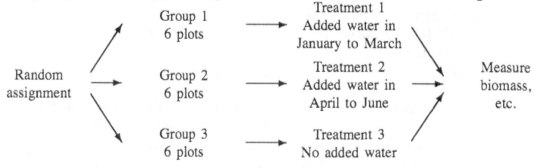

9.11 In a controlled scientific study, the effects of factors other than the nonphysical treatment (e.g., the placebo effect, differences in the prior health of the subjects) can be eliminated or accounted for, so that the differences in improvement observed between the subjects can be attributed to the differences in treatments.

9.13 (a) The researchers simply observed the diets of subjects; they did not alter them. (That is, no treatments were assigned.) **(b)** Such language is reasonable because with observational studies, no "cause-and-effect" conclusion would be reasonable.

9.15 In this case, "lack of blindness" means that the experimenter knows which subjects were taught to meditate. He or she may have some expectation about whether or not meditation will lower anxiety; this could unconsciously influence the end-of-month assessment.

9.17 (a) The explanatory variable is the font; the response is the degree of agreement with the statement about healthiness. **(b)** *Completely randomized design:* 50 students are randomly assigned to each of the two fonts, and then they rate the healthiness of the product. **(c)** *Matched pairs design:* each student sees both fonts in random order, then rates the product's perceived healthiness for each font.

9.19 (a) Life satisfaction is observed; no treatments were imposed.

9.21 (b) All participating students had the same treatment.

9.23 (b)

9.25 (a) The researchers did not randomly assign where the people lived, so no treatments were actively imposed.

9.27 (a) The choice should be made randomly.

9.29 (a) This is an observational study; the subjects chose their own "treatments" (how much red meat to eat). The explanatory variable is red meat consumption, and the response variable is whether or not a subject dies. (There may have been other variables, but these were the only ones mentioned in the problem.) **(b)** Many answers are possible. For example, smoking is known to increase the risk of cancer. These variables are called lurking variables. **(c)** Many answers are possible. For example, how many servings of fruits and vegetables were consumed along with the red meat?

9.31 This is an experiment, because the treatment is selected (randomly, we assume) by the interviewer. The explanatory variable (treatment) is the level of identification, and the response variable is whether or not the interview is completed.

9.33 (a) In an observational study, we simply observe subjects who live near highways and compare them with others who do live near highways. In an experiment, we would *assign* where the subjects live. **(b)** Answers will vary. For example, those who live near highways might have less money and be attracted to the (possibly) lower housing costs near a highway. Money (available for housing and health care) would be a variable that might be confounding. **(c)** No. Who would want their housing situation randomly assigned? **Note:** It is probably not ethical to randomly assign whether a person lives near a highway or not.

See Chapter 10 – Data Ethics for more details on ethical considerations.

9.35 (a) Diagram follows. **(b)** Assign labels 001 to 120. If using Table B, line 108 gives 090, 009, 067, 092, 041, 059, 040, 080, 029, 091.

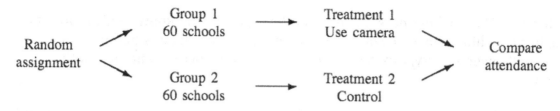

9.37 (a) The outline is shown. **(b)** From line 120, we choose subjects corresponding to the numbers 16, 04, 26, 21, 19, 07, 22, 10, 25, 13, 15, 05, 29, 09, 08 for the first group, and the rest for group 2. Thus, the marijuana group consists of Mattos, Bower, Williams, Sawant, Reichert, DeVore, Scannell, Giriunas, Stout, Kennedy, Mani, Burke, Zaccai, Fritz, and Fleming. All other subjects are assigned to the non-marijuana group. **(c)** This could be a double-blind experiment, assuming that subjects can't distinguish between the types of marijuana smoked, and the persons measuring output and earnings of subjects don't know what kind of marijuana a subject smoked. Ensuring these conditions is very unlikely.

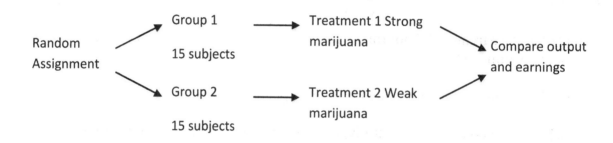

9.39 (a) There are two factors. The first factor is type of granola, and has two levels (regular and low-fat). The second factor is serving size label, and has three levels (2 servings, 1 serving, and no label). There are six treatment combinations (regular granola at 2 servings, regular granola at 1 serving, regular granola with no serving label, low-fat granola with 2 servings, low-fat granola with 1 serving, and low-fat granola with no serving label). At 20 subjects per treatment, there were 120 subjects in the experiment. **(b)**

	Granola type	
Serving size label	Regular	Low-fat
2 servings	20 subjects	20 subjects
1 serving	20 subjects	20 subjects
No label	20 subjects	20 subjects

9.41 The factors are pill type and spray type. "Double-blind" means that the treatment assigned to a patient was unknown to both the patient and those responsible for assessing the effectiveness of that treatment. "Placebo-controlled" means that some of the subjects were given placebos. Even though placebos possess no medical properties, some subjects may show improvement or benefits just as a result of participating in the experiment; the placebos allow those doing the study to observe this effect.

9.43 (a) The subjects are randomly chosen (preferably people who like flavored water). Each subject tastes two cups of flavored water, in identical unlabeled cups. One contains MiO, the other the ready-to-drink product. The cups are presented in random order: half the subjects get MiO, then the ready-to-drink; the other half, the ready-to-drink, then MiO. Each subject says which cup he or she prefers; preference is the response variable. **(b)** We must assign 10 customers to get regular coffee first. Label the subjects 01 to 20. Starting at line 138, the "MiO first" group is: 16, 08, 15, 13, 17, 04, 10, 19, 12, and 18.

9.45 Each player will be put through the sequence (100 yards, four times) twice—once with oxygen and once without. For each player, randomly determine whether to use oxygen on the first or second trial. Allow ample time (perhaps a day or two) between trials for full recovery.

9.47 The diagram is shown. The last stage ("Observe heart health") might be described in more detail.

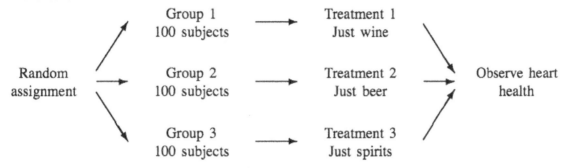

9.49 Any experiment randomized in this way assigns all the women to one treatment and all the men to the other. That is, sex is completely confounded with treatment. If women and men respond differently to the treatment, the experiment will be strongly biased. The direction of the bias is random, depending on the coin toss.

9.51 (a) "Randomized" means that patients were randomly assigned to receive either SAMe or a placebo. "Double-blind" means that the treatment assigned to a patient was unknown to both the patient and those responsible for assessing the effectiveness of that treatment. Even though placebos possess no medical properties, some subjects may show improvement or benefits just as a result of participating in the experiment; the placebos allow those doing the study to observe this effect. **(b)** Statistical significance means that the SAMe group had a greater difference in response (more had a positive response) than could be attributed to chance. This means that it appears SAMe helps reduce depression when used with standard treatment. **(c)** Diagram below.

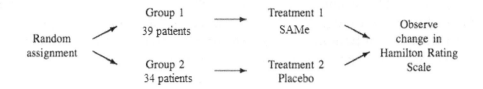

9.53 is a Web-based exercise.

Chapter 10 – Data Ethics

As the text states, "Most of these exercises pose issues for discussion. There are no right or wrong answers, but there are more and less thoughtful answers." We have not tried to supply answers for exercises that are largely matters of opinion. For that reason, only a few solutions are provided here.

10.1 These six proposals are clearly in increasing order of risk. Most students will consider that option (a) qualifies as minimal risk, and most will agree that option (e) goes beyond minimal risk. Opinions will vary on where to "draw the line," of course.

10.3 Many students will see both situations as coercive. Certainly, the prospect of losing needed health services would induce most subjects to agree to participate. Likewise, an employee's "voluntary" participation might be rewarded (or penalized) in job performance evaluations.

10.11 Most students will see option (a) as allowable, option (b) as questionable even though the meetings are public, and option (c) as not allowable due to the psychologist "pretending to be converted."

Chapter 11 – Producing Data: Part II Review

Test Yourself Exercise Answers are answers or sketches. All of these problems are similar to ones found in Chapters 8–10, for which the solutions in this manual provide more detail.

11.1 (c) hives with bees;hives with no bees; no hives

11.3 (a) Label the students 01 through 35 alphabetically (down the columns). **(b)** Using Table B and starting on line 115, the selected students are 04 = Bower, 17 = Huling, 32 = Vore, 22 = Newburg, 09 = Ding, and 26 = Pulak. **(c)** The response variable is "How much I trust the Internet for health information."

11.5 (d)

11.7 (a) No treatments were assigned by the researchers.

11.9 Many answers are possible. One possible lurking variable is "student attitude about the purpose of college" (students with a view that college is about partying, rather than studying, may be more likely to binge drink and more likely to have lower grades). Remember that a correct example of a lurking variable *must* be a variable that simultaneously drives both "GPA" and "binge drinking" together.

11.11 (d) 30-second once, 30-second twice, 45-second once, 45-second twice, 60-second once, and 60-second twice

11.13 People who visit the *NOVA Science Now* Web site don't represent American adults broadly. Those people taking the survey went out of their way to participate in this online poll, and they read pro and con arguments after watching a program about the issue. It seems reasonable to believe that these people understand the issues better than most American adults.

11.15 (b) No treatments were assigned. Testing eyesight and IQ are not applying treatments.

11.17 (a) This is the definition of informed consent.

Supplementary Exercises

11.19 Placebos do work with real pain, so the placebo response tells nothing about the physical basis of the pain. In fact, placebos work poorly in hypochondriacs. The survey is described in the April 3, 1979, edition of the *New York Times*.

11.21 (a) increase **(b)** decrease **(c)** increase **(d)** decrease

Note: *The first and third statements make an argument in favor of a national health insurance system, while the second and fourth suggest reasons to oppose it*

11.23 (a) The factors are storage method (three levels: fresh, room temperature for one month, refrigerated for one month) and preparation method (two levels: cooked immediately, or after one hour). There are, therefore, six treatments (summarized in the table). The response variables are the tasters' color and flavor ratings. **(b)** Randomly allocate n potatoes to each of the six groups, and then compare ratings. **(c)** For each taster, randomly choose the order in which the fries are tasted. We'll note that tasters may become confused with six different batches to taste, however.

	Cooked immediately	Wait one hour
Fresh	1	2
Stored	3	4
Refrigerated	5	6

11.25 (a) This is an observational study; the subjects chose their own "treatments" (how much to drink). The explanatory variable is alcohol consumption, and the response variable is whether or not a subject dies. (There may have been other variables, but these were the only ones mentioned in the problem.) **(b)** Many answers are possible. For example, some nondrinkers might avoid drinking because of other health concerns. We do not know what kind of alcohol (beer? wine? whiskey?) the subjects were drinking.

Chapter 12 – Introducing Probability

12.1 In the long run, of a large number of five-card poker hands, the fraction in which you will be dealt a straight flush is about 1/64,974. It *does not* mean that exactly 1 out of 64,974 such hands would yield a straight flush. The probability of an event is the long-run frequency of times the event occurs if the experiment is repeated endlessly … not even almost 65,000 times.

12.3 (a) There are 21 zeros among the first 200 digits of the table (rows 101–105), for a proportion of 0.105. **(b)** Answers will vary, but more than 99% of all students should get between 7 and 33 heads out of 200 flips when $p = 0.1$.

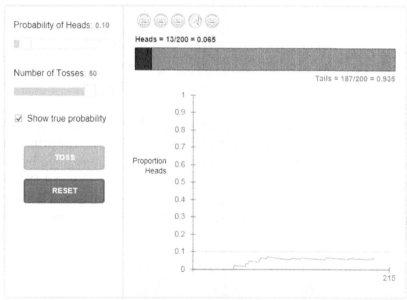

12.5 (a) S = {lives on campus, lives off campus}. **(b)** S = {All numbers between _____ and _____ years}. (Choices of upper and lower limits will vary, most likely due to the characteristics of your institution.) **(c)** S = {0000, 0001, 0002, … , 9999}. **(d)** S = {A, B, C, D, F} (students might also include W, "+", and "−").

12.7 For the sample space, add 1 to each pair total in the table shown in the previous solution: S = {3, 4, 5, 6, 7, 8, 9}. As all faces are equally likely and the dice are independent, each of the 16 possible pairings is equally likely, so (for example) the probability of a total of 5 is 3/16, because 3 pairings add to 4 (and then we add 1). The complete set of probabilities is shown in the table.

Total	Probability
3	1/16 = 0.0625
4	2/16 = 0.125
5	3/16 = 0.1875
6	4/16 = 0.25
7	3/16 = 0.1875
8	2/16 = 0.125
9	1/16 = 0.0625

12.9 (a) Event B specifically rules out obese subjects, so there is no overlap with event A. **(b)** A or B is the event "The person chosen is overweight or obese." $P(A$ or $B) = P(A) + P(B)$ $= 0.36 + 0.33 = 0.69$. **(c)** $P(C) = 1 - P(A$ or $B) = 1 - 0.69 = 0.31$.

12.11 (a) Disjoint. **(b)** Not disjoint; $300,000 is more than $100,000 and more than $250,000. **(c)** Disjoint; $3 + x$ cannot equal 3.

12.13 (a) $A = \{4, 5, 6, 7, 8, 9\}$, so $P(A) = 0.097 + 0.079 + 0.067 + 0.058 + 0.051 + 0.046 = 0.398$. **(b)** $B = \{2, 4, 6, 8\}$, so $P(B) = 0.176 + 0.097 + 0.067 + 0.051 = 0.391$. **(c)** A or $B = \{2, 4, 5, 6, 7, 8, 9\}$, so $P(A$ or $B) = 0.176 + 0.097 + 0.079 + 0.067 + 0.058 + 0.051 + 0.046 = 0.574$. This is different from $P(A) + P(B)$ because A and B are not disjoint.

12.15 (a) $P(Y \le 0.6) = 0.6$. **(b)** $P(Y < 0.6) = 0.6$. **(c)** $P(0.4 \le Y \le 0.8) = 0.4$. **(d)** $P(0.4 < Y \le 0.8) = 0.4$. The only difference between parts (c) and (d) is the inclusion of the point $Y = 0.4$. This has 0 probability for a continuous variable.

12.17 (a) This is $P(X \ge 35)$. **(b)** $P(X \ge 35) = P\left(Z > \dfrac{35 - 25.3}{6.5}\right) = P(Z \ge 1.49) = 1 - 0.9319 = 0.0681$ (using Table A).

12.19 (a) $Y \ge 8$ means the student runs the mile in 8 minutes or more. $P(Y \ge 8) = P(Z \ge \dfrac{8 - 7.11}{0.74}) = P(Z \ge 1.20) = 1 - 0.8849 = 0.1151$ (using Table A). **(b)** "The student could run the mile in less than 6 minutes" is the event $Y < 6$. $P(Y < 6) = P\left(Z < \dfrac{6 - 7.11}{0.74}\right) = P(Z < -1.50) = 0.0668$ (using Table A).

12.21 (a) If Joe says P(Syracuse wins) = 0.1, then he believes P(Duke wins) = 0.3 and P(North Carolina wins) = 0.2. **(b)** Joe's probabilities for Duke, Syracuse, and North Carolina add up to 0.6, so that leaves probability 0.4 for all other teams.

12.23 (b) The set $\{0, 1, 2, 3, 4, 5\}$ lists all possible counts.

12.25 (b) The other probabilities add to 0.97, so this must be 0.03.

12.27 (b) P(not Republican) = $1 - P$(Republican) = $1 - 0.25 = 0.75$.

12.29 (c) "7 or greater" means 7, 8, or 9—three of the ten possibilities.

12.31 (c) $Y > 1$ standardizes to $Z > 2.56$, for which Table A gives 0.0052.

12.33 (a) legitimate (even though it is not a "fair" die) **(b)** Legitimate (even if the deck of cards is not!) **(c)** not legitimate (the total is more than 1)

12.35 In computing the probabilities, we have dropped the trailing zeros from the land area figures. **(a)** P(area is forested) = $4176/9094 = 0.4592$ **(b)** P(area is not forested) = $1 - 0.4592 = 0.5408$

12.37 (a) The given probabilities add to 0.97, so other colors must account for the remaining 0.03. **(b)** P(white or silver) = $0.25 + 0.18 = 0.43$, so P(neither white nor silver) = $1 - 0.43 = 0.57$.

12.39 The probabilities of 2, 3, 4, and 5 are unchanged (1/6), so P(1 or 6) must still be 1/3. If $P(6) = 0.2$, then $P(1) = 1/3 - 0.2 = 2/15$.

Face	⚀	⚁	⚂	⚃	⚄	⚅
Probability	0.13	1/6	1/6	1/6	1/6	0.2

12.41 (a) It is legitimate because every person must fall into exactly one category, the probabilities are all between 0 and 1, and they add up to 1. **(b)** $0.169 = 0.002 + 0.008 + 0.153 + 0.006$ is the probability that a randomly chosen American is Hispanic. **(c)** $0.355 = 1 - 0.645$ is the probability that a randomly chosen American is *not* a non-Hispanic white.

12.43 (a) A corresponds to the outcomes in the first column or the third row. **(b)** Adding up those six outcomes gives $P(A) = 0.550$. This is different from the sum of the probabilities in parts (c) and (d) of Exercise 12.42 because that sum counts the overlap (0.168) twice.

12.45 (a) X is discrete, because it has a finite sample space. **(b)** "At least one nonword error" is the event $\{X \geq 1\}$ (or $\{X > 0\}$). $P(X \geq 1) = 1 - P(X = 0) = 0.9$. **(c)** $\{X \leq 2\}$ is "no more than two nonword errors," or "fewer than three nonword errors." $P(X \leq 2) = P(X = 0) + P(X = 1) + P(X = 2) = 0.1 + 0.2 + 0.3 = 0.6$. $P(X < 2) = P(X = 0) + P(X = 1) = 0.1 + 0.2 = 0.3$.

12.47 (a) There are ten pairs. Just using initials: {(A, D), (A, M), (A, S), (A, R), (D, M), (D, S), (D, R), (M, S), (M, R), (S, R)}. **(b)** Each has probability $1/10 = 10\%$. **(c)** Mei-Ling is chosen in four of the ten possible outcomes: $4/10 = 40\%$. **(d)** There are three pairs with neither Sam nor Roberto, so the probability is 3/10.

12.49 The possible values of Y are 1, 2, 3, ..., 12, each with probability 1/12. Aside from drawing a diagram showing all the possible combinations, one can reason that the first (regular) die is equally likely to show any number from 1 through 6. Half of the time, the second roll shows 0, and the other half it shows 6. Each possible outcome, therefore, has probability $(1/6)(1/2) = 1/12$.

12.51 (a) This is a continuous random variable because the set of possible values is an interval. **(b)** The height should be 1/2 because the area under the curve must be 1. (For a rectangle, area = L × W.) The density curve is illustrated. **(c)** $P(Y \leq 1) = 1/2$

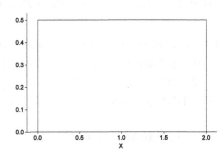

12.53 (a) $P(0.49 \leq V \leq 0.53) =$

$$P\left(\frac{0.49 - 0.51}{0.009} \leq Z \leq \frac{0.53 - 0.51}{0.009}\right) = P(-2.22 \leq Z \leq 2.22) =$$

$0.9868 - 0.0132 = 0.9736.$ **(b)** $P(V \leq 0.49) = P\left(Z \leq \frac{0.49 - 0.51}{0.009}\right) = P(Z \leq -2.22) = 0.0132.$

12.55 (a) Because there are 10,000 equally likely four-digit numbers (0000 through 9999), the probability of an exact match is $1/10{,}000 = 0.0001$. **(b)** There is a total of $24 = 4 \times 3 \times 2 \times 1$ arrangements of the four digits 5, 9, 7, and 4 (there are four choices for the first digit, three for the second, two for the third), so the probability of a match in any order is $24/10{,}000 = 0.0024$.

12.57 (a)–(c) Results will vary, but after n tosses, the distribution of the proportion (call it $\hat{p}$) is approximately Normal with mean 0.5 and standard deviation $1/(2\sqrt{n})$, while the distribution of the count of heads is approximately Normal with mean $0.5n$ and standard deviation $\sqrt{n}/2$. Therefore, using the 68–95–99.7 rule, we have the results shown in the table. Note that the range for the proportion $\hat{p}$ gets narrower, while the range for the count gets wider.

n	99.7% Range for $\hat{p}$	99.7% Range for count
40	0.5 ± 0.237	20 ± 9.5
120	0.5 ± 0.137	60 ± 16.4
240	0.5 ± 0.097	120 ± 23.2
480	0.5 ± 0.068	240 ± 32.9

12.59 (a) With $n = 50$, the variability in the proportion (call it $\hat{p}$) is larger. With $n = 100$, nearly all answers will be between 0.19 and 0.47. With $n = 400$, nearly all answers will be between 0.26 and 0.40. **(b)** Results will vary.

Chapter 13 – General Rules of Probability

13.1 It is unlikely that these events are independent. In particular, it is reasonable to expect that younger adults are more likely than older adults to be college students.

    Note: *Using the notation of conditional probability introduced later in this chapter, we believe* P(*college student | over 55*) < *0.08.*

13.3 If we assume that each site is independent of the others (and that they can be considered as a random sample from the collection of sites referenced in scientific journals), then P(all seven are still good) = $(1 - 0.13)^7 = (0.87)^7 = 0.3773$.

13.5 A Venn diagram is provided. B is the event "the degree is a bachelor's degree," and W is the event "the degree was earned by a woman." The probability of both W and B occurring is given. Subtracting this from the given probabilities for B and W gives the probabilities of the rest of those events. Those probabilities add to 0.80, so P(neither B nor W) = 0.20. **(a)** Because $P(W) = 0.59$, P(degree was earned by a man) = P(not W) = $1 - 0.59 = 0.41$, or 41%. **(b)** $P(B$ and not $W) =$

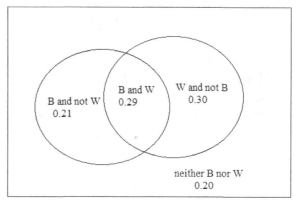

$0.50 - 0.29 = 0.21$, or 21%. **(c)** Because $P(B$ and $M) = 0.21$, but $P(B) \times P(M) = (0.50)(0.41) = 0.205$, then $P(B$ and $M) \neq P(B) \times P(M)$. So, B and M are not independent.

    Note: *While the multiplication here results in a "close" result to P(B and M), in the probabilistic sense, these must be **exactly** equal to have independence.*

13.7 Refer to the Venn diagram in the solution of Exercise 13.5. Using the notation given in Example 13.7, $P(W \mid B) = \dfrac{P(B \text{ and } W)}{P(B)} = \dfrac{0.29}{0.50} = 0.58$.

13.9 Let H be the event that an adult belongs to a club, and T be the event that he/she goes at least twice a week. We have been given $P(H) = 0.10$ and $P(T \mid H) = 0.40$. Note also that $P(T$ and $H) = P(T)$, because one has to be a member of the club in order to attend. So $P(T) = P(H)P(T \mid H) = (0.10)(0.40) = 0.04$. About 4% of all adults go to health clubs at least twice a week.

13.11 (a) and (b) These probabilities are provided in the table. **(c)** The product of these conditional probabilities gives the probability of a flush in spades by the general multiplication rule; we must draw a spade, and then another, and then a third, a fourth, and a fifth. The product of these probabilities is about 0.0004952. **(d)** Because there are four possible suits in which to have a flush, the probability of a flush is four times that found in part (c), or about 0.001981.

P(1st card is ♠)	13/52	= 0.25
P(2nd card is ♠ | first card is ♠)	12/51	= 0.2353
P(3rd card is ♠ | first two are ♠)	11/50	= 0.22
P(4th card is ♠ | first three are ♠)	10/49	= 0.2041
P(5th card is ♠ | first four are ♠)	9/48	= 0.1875

13.13 (a) The tree diagram is shown below. **(b)** Two branches result in a positive test result. Multiply out the probabilities on those branches and add to find P(positive test) = $(0.063)(0.21) + (0.937)(0.06) = 0.01323 + 0.05622 = 0.06945$.

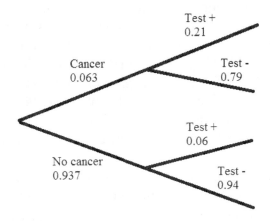

13.15 (a) P(no cancer \| positive test) = $\dfrac{P(\text{no cancer and positive test})}{P(\text{positive test})} = \dfrac{(0.937)(0.06)}{0.06945} = \dfrac{0.05622}{0.06945} =$ 0.8095. The 0.06945 in the denominator was found in Exercise 13.13. **(b)** About 81% of positive test results come from people without prostate cancer. Most of those being treated do not have the disease, and might suffer those serious side effects.

13.17 (b) This probability is $(1 – 0.02)^3 = (0.98)^3 = 0.9412$.

13.19 (a) P(at least one positive) = $1 – P$(both negative) = $1 – P$(first negative)P(second negative) = $1 – (0.1)(0.2) = 0.98$. Because the tests are independent, we can multiply the probabilities of a negative test on each.

13.21 (c) Of 4798 education doctorates, 1501 were awarded to males. Then $1501/4798 = 0.3128$.

13.23 (c) We want the fraction of engineering doctorates conferred to women. Outcome A (engineering doctorate) is what has been given (signaled by the phrase "of engineering doctorates").

13.25 (c) $P(W \text{ and } D) = P(W)P(D \mid W) = (0.86)(0.028) = 0.024$

13.27 $P(8 \text{ losses}) = (1 - 0.25)^8 = (0.75)^8 = 0.1001$

13.29 (a) $P(\text{win the jackpot}) = \left(\dfrac{1}{20}\right)\left(\dfrac{9}{20}\right)\left(\dfrac{1}{20}\right) = 0.001125$. **(b)** The other (non-cherry) symbol can show up on the middle wheel, with probability $\left(\dfrac{1}{20}\right)\left(\dfrac{11}{20}\right)\left(\dfrac{1}{20}\right) = 0.001375$, or on either of the outside wheels, with probability $= \left(\dfrac{19}{20}\right)\left(\dfrac{9}{20}\right)\left(\dfrac{1}{20}\right)$ (each). **(c)** Combining all three cases from part (b), we have $P(\text{exactly two cherries}) = 0.001375 + 2(0.021375) = 0.044125$.

13.31 PLAN: Let I be the event "infection occurs" and let F be "the repair fails." We have been given $P(I) = 0.03$, $P(F) = 0.14$, and $P(I \text{ and } F) = 0.01$. We want to find $P(\text{not } I \text{ and not } F)$. SOLVE: First use the general addition rule $P(I \text{ or } F) = P(I) + P(F) - P(I \text{ and } F) = 0.03 + 0.14 - 0.01 = 0.16$. This is the shaded region in the Venn diagram provided. Now observe that the desired probability is the complement of "I or F" (the *unshaded* region); $P(\text{not } I \text{ and not } F) = 1 - P(I \text{ or } F) = 0.84$. CONCLUDE: 84% of operations succeed and are free from infection.

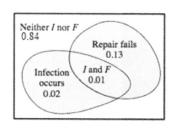

13.33 PLAN: Let I be the event "infection occurs" and let F be "the repair fails." Refer to the Venn diagram in Exercise 13.31 (ignoring the shading). We want to find $P(I \mid \text{not } F)$. SOLVE: We have $P(I \mid \text{not } F) = \dfrac{P(I \text{ and not } F)}{P(\text{not } F)} = \dfrac{0.02}{0.86} = 0.0233$. CONCLUDE: The probability of infection given that the repair is successful is 0.0233. That is, in 2.33% of all successful operation cases, the patient develops an infection.

13.35 (a) $P(\text{positive} \mid \text{disease}) = 564/574 = 0.9826$ **(b)** $P(\text{no disease} \mid \text{negative}) = 708/718 = 0.9861$

13.37 (a) These events are not independent, because $P(\text{pizza with mushrooms}) = 4/7$, but $P(\text{mushrooms} \mid \text{thick crust}) = 2/3$ (if the events were independent, these probabilities would be equal). Alternatively, note that $P(\text{thick crust with mushrooms}) = 2/7$, which is not equal to the product of $P(\text{mushrooms}) = 4/7$ and $P(\text{thick crust pizza}) = 3/7$. **(b)** With the eighth pizza, $P(\text{mushrooms}) = 4/8 = 1/2$, and $P(\text{mushrooms} \mid \text{thick crust}) = 2/4 = 1/2$, so these events are independent.

13.39 Let W be the event "the person is a woman" and M be "the person earned a Master's degree." **(a)** $P(\text{not } W) = 1569/3825 = 0.4102$ **(b)** $P(\text{not } W \mid M) = 322/816 = 0.3946$. **(c)** The events "choose a man" and "choose a Master's degree recipient" are not independent. If they were, the two probabilities in (a) and (b) would be equal.

13.41 Let D be the event "a seedling was damaged by a deer." **(a)** $P(D) = 209/871 = 0.2400$ **(b)** The conditional probabilities are
$P(D \mid \text{no cover}) = 60/211 = 0.2844$
$P(D \mid \text{cover} < 1/3) = 76/234 = 0.3248$

$P(D \mid 1/3 \text{ to } 2/3 \text{ cover}) = 44/221 = 0.1991$
$P(D \mid \text{cover} > 2/3) = 29/205 = 0.1415$
(c) Cover and damage are not independent; $P(D)$ decreases noticeably when thorny cover is 1/3 or more.

13.43 First, note that having no thorny cover means there is less than 1/3 thorny cover. So, this conditional probability is $P(\text{cover} < 1/3 \mid D) = (60 + 76)/(60 + 76 + 44 + 29) = 136/209 = 0.6507$, or 65.07%.

13.45 This is $P(A \text{ and } (\text{not } B) \text{ and } (\text{not } C)) = 0.35$.

13.47 (a) $P(\text{doubles on first toss}) = 1/6$, because 6 of the 36 equally likely outcomes enumerated in Figure 12.2 involve rolling doubles. **(b)** We need no doubles on the first roll (which happens with probability 5/6), then doubles on the second toss. $P(\text{first doubles appears on toss 2}) = (5/6)(1/6) = 5/36$. **(c)** Similarly, $P(\text{first doubles appears on toss 3}) = (5/6)^2(1/6) = 25/216$. **(d)** $P(\text{first doubles appears on toss 4}) = (5/6)^3(1/6)$, etc. In general, $P(\text{first doubles appears on toss } k) = (5/6)^{k-1}(1/6)$. **(e)** $P(\text{go again within 3 turns}) = P(\text{roll doubles in 3 or fewer rolls}) = P(\text{roll doubles on 1st, 2nd, or 3rd try}) = (1/6) + (5/6)(1/6) + (5/6)^2(1/6) = 0.4213$

13.49 PLAN: We construct a tree diagram showing the results (allergic or not) for each of the three individuals. SOLVE: In the tree diagram, each "up-step" represents an allergic individual (and has probability 0.02), and each "down-step" is a non-allergic individual (and has probability 0.98). At the end of each of the eight complete branches is the value of X. Any branch with two up-steps and one down-step has probability $0.02^2 \times 0.98^1 = 0.000392$, and yields $X = 2$. Any branch with one up-step and two down-steps has probability $0.02^1 \times 0.98^2 = 0.019208$, and yields $X = 1$.

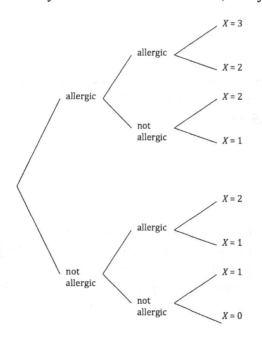

There are three branches each corresponding to $X = 2$ and $X = 1$, and only one branch each for $X = 3$ and $X = 0$. Because $X = 0$ and $X = 3$ appear on one branch each, $P(X = 0) = 0.98^3 = 0.941192$ and $P(X = 3) = 0.02^3 = 0.000008$. Meanwhile, $P(X = 1) = 3(0.02)^1(0.98)^2 = 0.057624$, and $P(X = 2) = 3(0.02)^2(0.98)^1 = 0.001176$. CONCLUDE: $P(X = 0) = 0.941192$, $P(X = 1) = 0.057624$, $P(X = 2) = 0.001176$, and $P(X = 3) = 0.000008$

13.51 $P(X = 2 \mid X \geq 1) = \dfrac{P(X = 2 \text{ and } X \geq 1)}{P(X \geq 1)} = \dfrac{P(X = 2)}{P(X \geq 1)} = \dfrac{0.001176}{1 - 0.941192} = 0.020$

13.53 Let R = {recent donor}, P = {pledged}, and C = {contributed}. (We could also give names to the "past donor" and "new prospect" events, but we do not need these for this explanation.) **(a)** The percent of calls resulting in a contribution can be found by considering all the branches of the tree that end in a contribution, meaning that we compute $P(C) = (0.5)(0.4)(0.8) + (0.3)(0.3)(0.6) + (0.2)(0.1)(0.5) = 0.224$, or 22.4%.
(b) $P(R \mid C) = = \dfrac{P(R \text{ and } C)}{P(C)} = \dfrac{(0.5)(0.4)(0.8)}{0.224} = 0.7143$, or 71.4%

13.55 The proportion having combination (16, 17) is $2(0.232)(0.213) = 0.098832$. (See Exercise 13.54 for the explanation of this calculation.)

13.57 If the DNA profile found on the hair is possessed by 1 in 1.6 million individuals, then we would expect about 3 individuals in the database of 4.5 million convicted felons to demonstrate a match. This comes from (4.5 million)/(1.6 million) = 2.8125, which was rounded up to 3.

13.59 is a Web-based exercise.

Section 13.7 Bayes' Rule (Optional)

13.7.1 $P(\text{false-negative}) = P(\text{disease present} \mid \text{negative test})$. Using the notation of Example 13.7.1, this is $P(B_1 \mid \text{not } A)$. From Figure 13.7.1, P(not A) = (0.063)(0.79) + (0.937)*(0.94) = 0.93055. So, $P(B_1 \mid \text{not } A)$ = (0.063)(0.79)/0.93055 = 0.0535.

13.7.3 A tree diagram is given below.

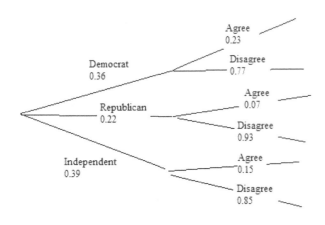

Multiply out the branches to find P(Agree) = (0.36)(0.23) + (0.22)(0.07) + (0.39)(0.15) = 0.1567. P(Democrat | Agree) = (0.36)(0.23)/0.1567 = 0.5284.

Chapter 14 – Binomial Distributions

14.1 Binomial. (1) We have a fixed number of observations ($n = 20$). (2) It is reasonable to believe that each call is independent of the others. (3) "Success" means reaching a working residential number; "failure" is any other outcome. (4) Each randomly dialed number has chance $p = 0.3$ of reaching a working residential number.

14.3 Not binomial. The trials aren't independent. If one tile in a box is cracked, there are likely more tiles cracked (probably due to rough handling of the box).

14.5 (a) C, the number caught, is binomial with $n = 10$ and $p = 0.7$. M, the number missed, is binomial with $n = 10$ and $p = 0.3$. **(b)** We find $P(M = 3) = \binom{10}{3}(0.3)^3(0.7)^7 =$

```
1-binomcdf(10,.3
,2)
        .6172172128
```

$120(0.027)(0.08235) = 0.2668$. With software, we find $P(M \geq 3) = 0.6172$. Here, we used the fact that the event "3 or more" is the complement of the event "2 or fewer" with graphing calculators and most software.

14.7 The screenshots below show Google's answers at the time these solutions were prepared. **(a)** 5 choose 2 returns 10. **(b)** 500 choose 2 returns 124,750, and 500 choose 100 returns 2.041694×10^{107}.
(c) (10 choose 1)*0.11*0.89^9 returns 0.38539204407.

5 choose 2 =	500 choose 2 =
10	**124750**

500 choose 100 =	(10 choose 1) * 0.11 * (0.89^9) =
2.041694e+107	**0.38539204407**

14.9 (a) X is binomial with $n = 10$ and $p = 0.3$; Y is binomial with $n = 10$ and $p = 0.7$ **(b)** The mean of Y is $(10)(0.7) = 7$ errors caught, and for X the mean is $(10)(0.3) = 3$ errors missed. **(c)** The standard deviation of Y (or X) is $\sigma = \sqrt{10(0.7)(0.3)} = 1.4491$ errors.

14.11 (a) $\mu = (1175)(0.37) = 434.75$ and $\sigma = \sqrt{1175(0.37)(1 - 0.37)} = \sqrt{273.8925} = 16.550$ students. **(b)** We observe that $np = (1175)(0.37) = 434.75 \geq 10$ and $n(1 - p) = (1175)(0.63) = 740.25 \geq 10$, so n is large enough for the Normal approximation to be reasonable. The college wants 450 students, so $P(X \geq 451) =$

$$P\left(Z \geq \frac{451 - 434.75}{16.550} \right) = P(Z \geq 0.98) = 0.1635.$$ **(c)** The exact binomial probability is 0.1706 (obtained from software), so the Normal approximation is 0.0071 (not quite three-fourths of 1%) too low. For a better approximation, consider using the continuity correction described in Exercise 14.43. **(d)** To decrease the chance of more students than they want, they need to decrease the number admitted (this will decrease both μ and σ). If $n = 1150$, then $\mu = (1150)(0.37) = 425.5$ and $\sigma = \sqrt{1150(0.37)(0.63)} = 16.373$, and the probability of more than 450 students is approximately 0.0597. Similar calculations with $n = 1140$ give $p = 0.0366$; with $n = 1145$, we have $p = 0.0471$; with $n = 1146$, we have $p = 0.0494$. They should admit, at most, 1146 students to have no more than a 5% chance of too many.

14.13 (b) He has three independent eggs, each with probability 1/4 of containing salmonella.

14.15 (c) The selections are not independent; once we choose one student, it changes the probability that the next student is a business major.

14.17 (b) This probability is $(0.25)(0.75)^3(0.25) = 0.0264$.

14.19 (b) The numbers 8 or 9 are two of the ten possible digits, so the probability is 0.20.

14.21 (a) The mean is $np = (80)(0.20) = 16$.

14.23 (a) A binomial distribution is *not* an appropriate choice for field goals made, because given the different situations the kicker faces (wind, distance, etc.), his probability of success is likely to change from one attempt to another. **(b)** It would be reasonable to use a binomial distribution for free throws made because each is from the same position with respect to the basket with no interference allowed for the shot, and presumably each is independent of any others.

14.25 (a) $n = 5$ and $p = 0.65$ **(b)** The possible values of X are the integers 0, 1, 2, 3, 4, 5. **(c)** All cases are computed:

$$P(X = 0) = \binom{5}{0}(0.65)^0(0.35)^5 = 0.00525 \qquad P(X = 1) = \binom{5}{1}(0.65)^1(0.35)^4 = 0.04877$$

$$P(X = 2) = \binom{5}{2}(0.65)^2(0.35)^3 = 0.18115 \qquad P(X = 3) = \binom{5}{3}(0.65)^3(0.35)^2 = 0.33642$$

$$P(X = 4) = \binom{5}{4}(0.65)^4(0.35)^1 = 0.31239 \qquad P(X = 5) = \binom{5}{5}(0.65)^5(0.35)^0 = 0.11603$$

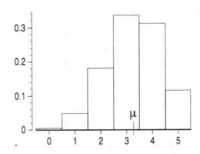

(d) $\mu = np = (5)(0.65) = 3.25$ and $\sigma = \sqrt{5(0.65)(1-0.65)} = 1.0665$ years. The mean μ is indicated on the probability histogram.

14.27 (a) All women are independent in terms of pregnancies—one woman getting pregnant will not affect whether another gets pregnant, and (we assume) each has the same probability of getting pregnant. **(b)** Under ideal conditions, the number who get pregnant is binomial with $n = 20$ and $p = 0.01$; $P(N \geq 1) = 1 - P(N = 0) = 1 - 0.8179 = 0.1821$. In typical use, $p = 0.03$, and $P(N \geq 1) = 1 - 0.5438 = 0.4562$.

14.29 (a) X, the number of women who get pregnant in typical use, is binomial with $n = 600$ and $p = 0.03$. The Normal approximation is safe: $np = 18$ and $n(1 - p) = 582$ are both at least 10. The mean is 18, and the standard deviation is 4.1785, so $P(X \geq 20) = P\left(Z \geq \dfrac{20-18}{4.1785}\right) = P(Z \geq 0.48) = 1 - 0.6844 = 0.3156$. The exact binomial probability is 0.3477. **(b)** Under ideal conditions, $p = 0.01$, so $np = 6$ is too small.

14.31 (a) If R is the number of red-blossomed plants out of a sample of 4, then $P(R = 3) = \dbinom{4}{3}(0.75)^3(0.25)^1 = 0.4219$, using a binomial distribution with $n = 4$ and $p = 0.75$. **(b)** With $n = 60$, the mean number of red-blossomed plants is $np = (60)(0.75) = 45$. **(c)** If R is the number of red-blossomed plants out of a sample of 60, then $P(R \geq 45) = P(Z \geq 0) = 0.5000$ (software gives 0.5688 using the binomial distribution).

14.33 (a) Of 720,783 total vehicles in these top four nameplates, Elantras accounted for a proportion of $247{,}912/720{,}783 = 0.3439$. **(b)** If E is the number of Elantra buyers in the 1000 surveyed buyers, then E has the binomial distribution with $n = 1000$, and $p = 0.3439$. $\mu = np = (1000)(0.3439) = 343.9$ and $\sigma = \sqrt{np(1-p)} = \sqrt{1000(0.3439)(1-0.3439)} = 15.021$ Elantra buyers. **(c)** $P(E < 400) = P(E \leq 399) = P(Z \leq -3.67) = 0.0001$.

14.35 (a) With $n = 100$, the mean and standard deviation are $\mu = 75$ and $\sigma = 4.3301$ questions, so $P(70 \leq X \leq 80) = P(-1.15 \leq Z \leq 1.15) = 0.7498$ (software gives 0.7518). **(b)** With $n = 250$, we have $\mu = 187.5$ and $\sigma = 6.8465$ questions, and a score between 70% and 80% means 175 to 200 correct answers, so $P(175 \leq X \leq 200) = P(-1.83 \leq Z$

≤ 1.83) = 0.9328 (software gives 0.9428).

Note: *If one used the more mathematical idea that "between" does not include the endpoints of the interval, we would have P(70 < X < 80) = P(71 ≤ X ≤ 79) = 0.6424 for the 100-question test and P(176 < X < 199) = 0.9328 for the 250-question test.*

14.37 (a) Answers will vary, but over 99.8% of samples should have 0 to 4 bad tomatoes. The result of one such sample by the applet is shown. **(b)** Each time we choose a sample of size 10, the probability that we have exactly 1 bad tomato is 0.3854; therefore, out of 20 samples, the number of times that we have exactly 1 bad tomato has a binomial distribution with parameters $n = 20$ and $p = 0.3854$. This means that most students—99.8% of them—will find that between 2 and 14 of their 20 samples have exactly 1 bad tomato, giving a proportion between 0.10 and 0.70. (If anyone has an answer outside of that range, it would be significant evidence that he or she did the exercise incorrectly.)

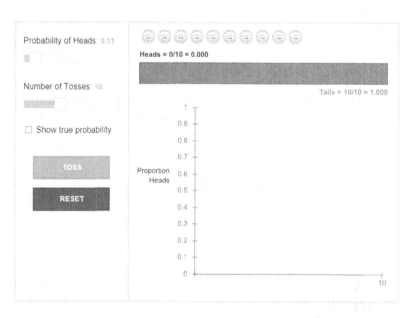

14.39 The number N of infections among untreated BJU students (assuming independence) is binomial with $n = 1400$ and $p = 0.80$, so the mean is 1120 and the standard deviation is 14.9666 students. In addition, 75% of that group is 1050, and the Normal approximation is safe because $(1400)(0.80) = 1120$ and $(1400)(0.20) = 280$ are both at least 10. $P(N \geq 1050) = P\left(Z \geq \dfrac{1050 - 1120}{14.9666} \right) = P(Z \geq -4.68)$, which is very near to 1. (Exact binomial computation gives 0.999998.)

14.41 Define V and U as in the previous exercise. **(a)** $P(V = 1) = 0.3741$ and $P(U = 1) = 0.0960$. Because these events are (assumed) independent, $P(V = 1$ and $U = 1) = P(V = 1)P(U = 1) = (0.3741)(0.0960) = 0.0359$. **(b)** Considering all the possible ways to have a total of two infections, we have $P(2$ infections$) = P(V = 0$ and $U = 2) + P(V = 1$ and $U = 1) + P(V = 2$ and $U = 0) = P(V = 0)P(U = 2) + P(V = 1)P(U = 1) + P(V = 2)P(U = 0) = (0.4181)(0.3840) + (0.3741)(0.0960) + (0.1575)(0.0080) = 0.1977$.

14.43 The number X of fairways Tiger hits is binomial, with $n = 30$ and $p = 0.63$. **(a)** $np = 18.9$ and $n(1 - p) = 11.1$, so the Normal approximation is (barely) safe. **(b)** The mean is $np = 18.9$, and the standard deviation is $\sqrt{30(0.63)(0.37)} = 2.6444$. Using the Normal approximation, $P(X \geq 23) = P(Z \geq 1.55) = 0.0606$. **(c)** With the continuity correction, $P(X \geq 23) = P(X \geq 22.5) = P(Z \geq 1.36) = 0.0869$ (using Table A). Indeed, the answer using the continuity correction is closer to the exact answer (0.0838).

14.45 is a Web-based exercise.

Chapter 15 – Sampling Distributions

15.1 Both are statistics; they came from the 11 subjects in the experiment.

15.3 98.8% and 22 are statistics; they are based on the survey of 500 American anabolic androgenic steroid users; 50.0% is a parameter (it is true for all Americans ages 16 to 62).

15.5 Although the probability of having to pay for a total loss for one or more of the 12 policies is very small, if this were to happen, it would be financially disastrous. On the other hand, for thousands of policies, the law of large numbers says that the average claim on many policies will be close to the mean, so the insurance company can be assured that the premiums it collects will (almost certainly) cover claims.

15.7 (a) The histogram is provided.
(b) The mean is $\mu = 69.4$. **(c) and (d)** Results will vary. The results of one sample are shown. This sample selects students 5, 2, 9, and 4, with scores of 72, 63, 75, and 55. Their mean is
$\bar{x} = (72 + 63 + 75 + 55) / 4 = 66.25$.
Students should repeat this process until they have 10 sample means.

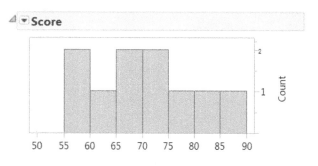

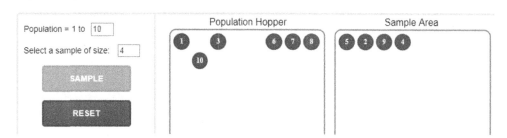

15.9 (a) The sampling distribution of $\bar{x}$ is $N(115, 25/\sqrt{100}) = N(115$ mg/dl, 2.5 mg/dl). Therefore, $P(112 < \bar{x} < 118) = P(-1.2 < Z < 1.2) = 0.8849 - 0.1151 = 0.7698$, using Table A. **(b)** With $n = 1000$, the sample mean has the $N(115$ mg/dl, 0.7906 mg/dl) distribution, so $P(112 < x < 118) = P(-3.79 < Z < 3.79) = 0.9998$.

15.11 No. The histogram of the sample values will look like the population distribution, whatever it might happen to be. (For example, if we roll a fair die many times, the histogram of sample values should look relatively flat—probability close to 1/6 for each value 1, 2, 3, 4, 5, and 6.) The central limit theorem says that the histogram of *sample means* (from many large samples) will look more and more Normal.

15.13 STATE: We ask, what is the probability that the average loss for 10,000 such policies will be no greater than \$135, when the long-run average loss is \$125? PLAN: Use the central limit theorem to approximate this probability. SOLVE: The central limit theorem says that, in spite of the skewness of the population distribution, the average loss among 10,000 policies will be approximately $N(\$125, \$300/\sqrt{10{,}000})$ = $N(\$125, \$3)$. Now, $P(\bar{x} \le \$135) = P(Z \le \frac{135-125}{3}) = P(Z \le 3.33) = 0.9996$.

CONCLUDE: We can be about 99.96% certain that average losses will not exceed \$135 per policy.

15.15 Answers will vary due to randomness. **(a)** One repetition of 25 sample means resulted in the histogram shown. **(b)** $\bar{x} = 76$ never occurred in any of these samples. **(c)** The mean for these four students is 76. Because a sample mean of 76 (or higher) never occurred, we might conclude that the mean score for the four honors students was unusually high (that is, that mean is "statistically significant").

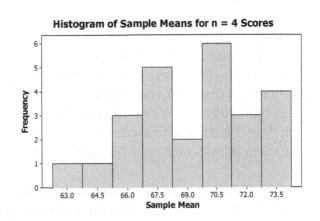

Histogram of Sample Means for n = 4 Scores

Note: *1000 repetitions of samples of size 4 found that a mean of 76 was higher than the maximum sample mean (75.333). We can conclude that the estimated probability of this sample mean occurring is less than 0.001.*

15.17 (b) statistic; this is a proportion of the people interviewed in the sample of 60,000 households.

15.19 (b) The law of large numbers says that the mean from a large sample is close to the population mean. Statement (c) is also true, but is based on the central limit theorem, not on the law of large numbers.

15.21 (c) The standard deviation of the distribution of $\bar{x}$ is $\sigma/\sqrt{n}$.

15.23 (c) The central limit theorem says that the mean from a large sample has (approximately) a Normal distribution. Statement (a) is also true, but is based on the law of large numbers, not on the central limit theorem.

15.25 1 is a parameter (the mean of the population of all conductivity measurements); 1.07 is a statistic (the mean of the 10 measurements in the sample).

15.27 In the long run, the gambler earns an average of 94.7 cents per bet. In other words, the gambler loses (and the house gains) an average of 5.3 cents for each \$1 bet.

15.29 Let X be Shelia's measured glucose level. **(a)** $P(X > 130) = P(Z > 0.67) = 0.2514$ **(b)** If $\bar{x}$ is the mean of four measurements (assumed to be independent), then $\bar{x}$ has an $N(122, 12/\sqrt{4}) = N(122$ mg/dl, 6 mg/dl) distribution, and $P(\bar{x} > 130) = P(Z > 1.33) = 0.0918$.

15.31 As shown in Exercise 15.29(b), the mean of four measurements has an $N(122$ mg/dl, 6 mg/dl) distribution, and $P(Z > 1.645) = 0.05$ if Z is $N(0,1)$, so $L = 122 + 1.645 \times 6 = 131.87$ mg/dl.

15.33 (a) $\bar{x}$ will have an approximately Normal distribution with mean 8.8 beats per five seconds, and standard deviation $1/\sqrt{24} = 0.204124$ beats per five seconds. **(b)** $P(\bar{x} < 8) = P(Z < -3.92)$, essentially 0. **(c)** If the total number of beats in one minute is less than 100, then the average over twelve five-second intervals needs to be less than $100/12 = 8.333$ beats per five seconds. $\bar{x}$ will have an approximately Normal distribution with mean 8.8 beats per five seconds, and standard deviation $1/\sqrt{12} = 0.288675$ beats per five seconds. $P(\bar{x} < 8.333) = P(Z < -1.62) = 0.0526$

15.35 STATE: What are the probabilities of an average return over 10%, or less than 5%? PLAN: Use the central limit theorem to approximate this probability. SOLVE: The central limit theorem says that over 40 years, $\bar{x}$ (the mean return) is approximately Normal with mean $\mu = 13.3\%$ and standard deviation $17.0\%/\sqrt{40} = 2.688\%$. Therefore, $P(\bar{x} > 10\%) = P(Z > -1.23) = 0.8907$, and $P(\bar{x} < 5\%) = P(Z < -3.09) = 0.0010$. CONCLUDE: There is about an 89% chance of getting average returns over 10%, and a 0.01% chance of getting average returns less than 5%.
    Note: *We have to assume that returns in separate years are independent.*

15.37 We need to choose n so that $6.5/\sqrt{n} = 1$. That means $\sqrt{n} = 6.5$, so $n = 42.25$. Because n must be a whole number, take $n = 43$.

15.39 On the average, Joe loses 40 cents each time he plays (that is, he spends $1 and gets back 60 cents).

15.41 (a) With $n = 150{,}000$, $\mu_{\bar{x}} = \$0.40$ and $\sigma_{\bar{x}} = \$18.96/\sqrt{150{,}000} = \$0.0490$. **(b)** $P(\$0.30 < \bar{x} < \$0.50) = P(-2.04 < Z < 2.04) = 0.9586$

15.43 The mean is $10.5 = (3)(3.5)$ because a single die has a mean of 3.5. Sketches will vary, as will the number of rolls; one result is shown.

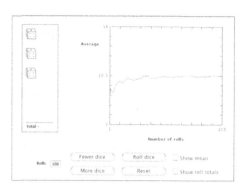

15.45 is a Web-based exercise.

Chapter 16 – Confidence Intervals: The Basics

16.1 (a) The sampling distribution of $\bar{x}$ has mean μ (unknown) and standard deviation $\dfrac{\sigma}{\sqrt{n}} = \dfrac{125}{\sqrt{170,100}} = 0.3031$. **(b)** According to this rule, 95% of all values of $\bar{x}$ fall within 2 standard deviations of the sampling distribution of μ (that is, within $2(0.3031) = 0.6062$). **(c)** 285 ± 0.6062, or between 284.3938 and 285.6062

16.3 Shown below are sample output screens for (a) 10 and (b) 1000 SRS's. In 99.7% of all repetitions of part (a), students should see between 5 and 10 hits (that is, at least 5 of the 10 SRS's capture the true mean μ). Out of 1000 80% confidence intervals, nearly all students will observe between 76% and 84% capturing the mean. This result had 81% of the 1000 intervals containing the mean.

16.5 Search Table A for 0.1250 (half of the 25% that is not included in the middle, shaded area corresponding to 75% confidence). This area corresponds to $-z^* = -1.15$, or $z^* = 1.15$.

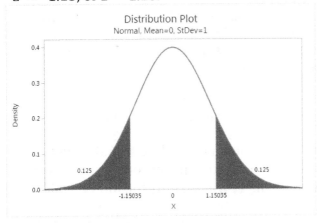

16.7 (a) A stemplot is provided. The two low scores (72 and 74) are both possible outliers, but there are no other apparent deviations from Normality. **(b)** STATE: What is the mean IQ μ of all seventh-grade girls in this school district? PLAN: We will estimate μ by giving a

99% confidence interval. SOLVE: The problem states that these girls are an SRS of the population, which is very large, so conditions for inference are met. In part (a), we saw that the scores are consistent with having come from a Normal population. With $\bar{x} = 105.84$ and $z^* = 2.576$, our 99% confidence interval for μ is given by

$$105.84 \pm 2.576\frac{15}{\sqrt{31}} = 105.84 \pm 6.94 = 98.90 \text{ to } 112.78 \text{ IQ}$$

points. CONCLUDE: We are 99% confident that the mean IQ of seventh-grade girls in this district is between 98.90 and 112.78 points.

Stem-and-leaf of IQ N = 31
Leaf Unit = 1

2	7	24
2	7	
2	8	
4	8	69
6	9	13
8	9	68
14	10	023334
(3)	10	578
14	11	11222444
6	11	89
4	12	0
3	12	8
2	13	02

16.9 With $z^* = 1.96$ and $\sigma = 7.5$, the margin of error is $z^*\dfrac{\sigma}{\sqrt{n}} = \dfrac{14.7}{\sqrt{n}}$.

(a) and (b) The margins of error are given in the table. **(c)** Margin of error decreases as n increases. (Specifically, every time the sample size n is quadrupled, the margin of error is halved.)

n	m.e.
100	1.47
400	0.735
1600	0.3675

16.11 (c) $z = 3.291$. Using Table A, search for 0.9995.

16.13 (b) As the confidence level increases, z^* increases. This makes the margin of error larger.

16.15 (b) The standard deviation of $\bar{x}$ is $\dfrac{\sigma}{\sqrt{n}} = \dfrac{125}{\sqrt{900}} = 4.167$.

16.17 (b) As the confidence level increases, z^* increases. This makes the margin of error larger.

16.19 (a) We use $\bar{x} \pm z^*\dfrac{\sigma}{\sqrt{n}}$, or $15.3 \pm 2.576\dfrac{8.5}{\sqrt{463}} = 15.3 \pm 1.018 = 14.282 \text{ to } 16.318$

hours. **(b)** The 463 students in this class must be a random sample of all of the first-year students at this university to satisfy conditions for inference.

16.21 The margin of error is now $2.576\dfrac{8.5}{\sqrt{464}} = 1.02$, so the extra observation has minimal impact on the margin of error (the sample was large to begin with). If $\bar{x} = 36.8$, then the 99% confidence interval for average amount of time spent studying becomes $36.8 \pm 1.02 = 35.78 \text{ to } 37.82$ hours. The outlier had a huge impact on $\bar{x}$, which shifts the interval a lot.

16.23 This student is also confused. If we repeated the sample over and over, 95% of all future sample means would be within 1.96 standard deviations of μ (that is, within 1.96 $\dfrac{\sigma}{\sqrt{n}}$) of the true, unknown value of μ. Future samples will have no memory of our sample.

16.25 (a) A stemplot of the data is provided. The distribution is noticeably skewed to the left. The data do not appear to follow a Normal distribution. **(b)** STATE: What is the mean load μ required to pull apart pieces of Douglas fir? PLAN: We will estimate μ by giving a 95% confidence interval. SOLVE: The problem states that we are willing to take this sample to be an SRS of the population. In spite of the shape of the stemplot, we are told to assume that this distribution is Normal with standard deviation $\sigma = 3000$ lbs. We find $\bar{x} = 30{,}841$ lbs, so the 95% confidence interval for μ is given by $30{,}841 \pm 1.96$ $\dfrac{3000}{\sqrt{20}} = 30{,}841 \pm 1314.81 = 29{,}526.19$ to $32{,}155.81$ pounds.

CONCLUDE: With 95% confidence, the mean load μ required to break apart pieces of Douglas fir is between 29,526.2 and 32,155.8 pounds; however, given the shape of the distribution of the data, we cannot rely much on this interval.

Stem and Leaf

Stem	Leaf	Count
33	0237	4
32	033677	6
31	399	3
30	259	3
29		
28	7	1
27		
26	5	1
25		
24	1	1
23	0	1

23|0 represents 23000

16.27 (a) A stemplot is given. There is little evidence that the sample does not come from a Normal distribution. For inference, we must assume that the 10 untrained students were selected randomly from the population of all untrained people. **(b)** STATE: What is the average (mean) DMS odor threshold, μ, for all untrained people? PLAN: We will estimate μ with a 95% confidence interval. SOLVE: We have assumed that we have a random sample, and that the population from which we are sampling is Normal. We obtain $\bar{x} = 29.4$ μ g/l. Our 95% confidence interval for μ is given by $29.4 \pm 1.96\dfrac{7}{\sqrt{10}} = 29.4 \pm 4.34 = 25.06$ to 33.74 μg/l. CONCLUDE: With 95% confidence, the mean sensitivity for all untrained people is between 25.06 and 33.74 μg/l.

```
Stem-and-leaf of DMS N = 10
Leaf Unit = 1
   1    1   9
   3    2   23
   4    2   9
  (4)   3   0013
   2    3   5
   1    4   2
```

16.29 is a Web-based exercise.

Chapter 17 – Tests of Significance: The Basics

17.1 (a) If $\mu = 50$, the distribution is approximately Normal with mean $\mu = 50$ and standard deviation

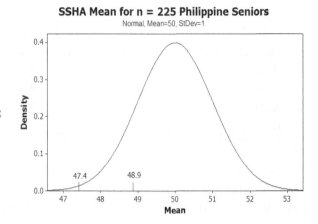

SSHA Mean for n = 225 Philippine Seniors
Normal, Mean=50, StDev=1

$\frac{\sigma}{\sqrt{n}} = \frac{15}{\sqrt{225}} = 1$. **(b)** The actual result lies out toward the low tail of the curve, while 48.9 is fairly close to the middle. If $\mu = 50$, observing a value similar to 48.9 would not be too surprising, but 47.4 is much less likely, and it therefore provides some evidence that $\mu < 50$.

17.3 $H_0 : \mu = 50$ vs. $H_a : \mu < 50$. Because the teacher suspects that poor attitudes are, in part, responsible for the decline in scores, we look to see if attitude scores are decreasing.

17.5 $H_0 : \mu = 75$ vs. $H_a : \mu < 75$. The professor suspects this section's students perform worse than the population of all students in the class on average.

17.7 Hypotheses are statements about parameters, not statistics. The research question is not about the sample mean ($\bar{x}$), but should be about the population mean, μ.

17.9 (a) With $\sigma = 60$ and $n = 18$, the standard deviation is $\frac{\sigma}{\sqrt{n}} = \frac{60}{\sqrt{18}} = 14.1421$, so when $\mu = 0$, the distribution of $\bar{x}$ is $N(0, 14.1421)$. **(b)** The P-value is $P = 2P(\bar{x} \geq 17) =$

$2P\left(Z \geq \frac{17 - 0}{14.1421}\right) = 0.2302$.

17.11 (a) The P-value for $\bar{x} = 48.7$ is 0.1357. This is not significant at either $\alpha = 0.05$ or $\alpha = 0.01$. **(b)** The P-value for $\bar{x} = 47.4$ is 0.0047. This is significant at both $\alpha = 0.05$ and $\alpha = 0.01$. **(c)** If $\mu = 50$ (that is, if H_0 were true), observing a value similar to 48.7 would not be too surprising, but 47.4 is much less likely, and it therefore provides strong evidence that $\mu < 50$.

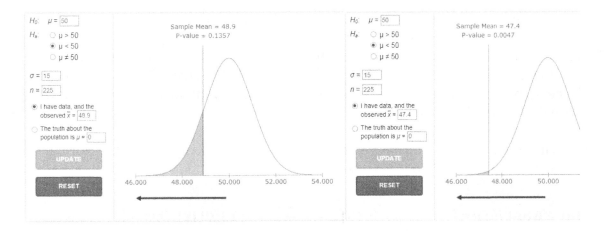

17.13 (a) $z = \dfrac{0.3-0}{1/\sqrt{10}} = \dfrac{0.3-0}{0.3162} = 0.9488$ **(b)** $z = \dfrac{1.02-0}{1/\sqrt{10}} = \dfrac{1.02-0}{0.3162} = 3.226$

(c) $z = \dfrac{17-0}{60/\sqrt{18}} = \dfrac{17-0}{14.1421} = 1.2021$; note that in part (c), the test is two-sided, while in parts (a) and (b), it is one-sided.

17.15 STATE: Is there evidence that the average percentage tip when bad news is received (a bad weather prediction) is less than 20%? PLAN: Let μ be the average percentage tip for all customers receiving bad news. We test $H_0: \mu = 20$ against $H_a: \mu < 20$ because we wonder if the value of μ is less than 20%. SOLVE: We have a sample of $n = 20$ customers, and observe $\bar{x} = 18.19\%$. The standard deviation of $\bar{x}$ is $\dfrac{2}{\sqrt{20}} = 0.4472$, so the test statistic is

$z = \dfrac{18.19 - 20}{0.4472} = -4.05$. The P-value is $P(Z \leq -4.05) \approx 0$. CONCLUDE: There is overwhelming evidence that the average tip percentage when bad news is delivered is lower than the average tip percentage overall. Random chance does not explain the small value of $\bar{x}$ observed.

17.17 This is not significant at the $\alpha = 0.05$ level because z is not larger than 1.96 or less than −1.96. It is also not significant at $\alpha = 0.01$ because $|z|$ is smaller than 2.576.

17.19 Using Figure 17.7, it appears that six samples had a median of 33, three had a median of 34, and we were told that eight had a median of 35 or larger. That means the estimated P-value is $17/1000 = 0.017$. If the median had been 30, we'd estimate a P-value of about 0.109 (about 50 samples had a median of 30, 30 had a median of 31, and 12 had a median of 32).

17.21 (a) This is the definition of a P-value.

17.23 (c) The P-value for $z = 2.41$ is 0.0080 (assuming that the difference is in the correct direction; that is, assuming that the alternative hypothesis was $H_a\ \mu > \mu_0$).

17.25 (a) The null hypothesis states that μ takes on the "default" value, 18 seconds.

17.27 (c) A small *P*-value means we should not (or should rarely) find an observed difference that is as large as or larger than what was seen in H_0 is true. The *P*-value does not tell us whether the difference seen is "large" or "practically important," nor does it refer to the probability that H_0 is true.

17.29 (a) This is a one-sided alternative, so we have 0.005 in the right tail of the Normal distribution, leading to $z > 2.576$.

17.31 (a) We test $H_0: \mu = 0$ vs. $H_a: \mu > 0$. **(b)** $z = \dfrac{2.35 - 0}{2.5/\sqrt{200}} = 13.29$ **(c)** This value of z is far outside the range we would expect from the $N(0,1)$ distribution. Under H_0, it would be virtually impossible to observe a sample mean as large as 2.35, based on a sample of 200 men. The sample mean is not explained by random chance, and we would easily reject H_0.

17.33 "$P < 0.05$" *does* mean that H_0 is not likely to be correct ... but only in the sense that it provides a poor explanation of the data observed. It means that if H_0 is true, a sample as contrary to H_0 as our sample would occur by chance alone less than 5% of the time, if the experiment was repeated over and over. However, it does *not* mean that there is a less than 5% chance that H_0 is true.

17.35 The person making the objection is confusing practical significance with statistical significance. In fact, a 5% increase isn't a lot in a pragmatic sense. However, $P = 0.03$ means that random chance does not easily explain the difference observed. That is, there does seem to be an increase in mean improvement for those who expressed their anxieties ... but the significance test does not address whether the difference is large enough to matter. Statistical significance is not practical significance.

17.37 In the sketch, the "significant at 1%" region includes only the dark shading ($z > 2.326$). The "significant at 5%" region of the sketch includes both the light and dark shading ($z > 1.645$). When a test is significant at the 1% level, it means that if

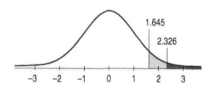

the null hypothesis were true, outcomes similar to (or more extreme than) those seen are expected less than once in 100 repetitions of the experiment. When a test is significant at the 5% level, it means that if the null hypothesis were true, outcomes similar to (or more extreme than) those seen are expected less than 5 in 100 repetitions of the experiment. Significance at the 1% level implies significance at the 5% level (or at any level higher than 1%). The converse is false: something that occurs "less than 5 times in 100 repetitions" is not necessarily as rare as something that happens "less than once in 100 repetitions," so a test that is significant at the 5% level is not necessarily significant at the 1% level. Any z test statistic between 1.645 and 2.326 will be significant at the 5% level, but not at the 1% level.

17.39 Because a *P*-value is a probability, it can never be greater than 1. The correct *P*-value is $P(Z \geq 1.33) = 0.0918$.

17.41 STATE: What is the mean percent change μ in spinal mineral content of nursing mothers? PLAN: We will test the hypotheses H_0: $\mu = 0\%$ against H_a: $\mu < 0\%$. SOLVE: The sample mean is $\bar{x} = -3.587\%$. The test statistic is $z = \dfrac{-3.587 - 0}{2.5/\sqrt{47}} = -9.84,$ and the *P*-value is $P(Z \leq -9.84) \approx 0$. CONCLUDE: There is overwhelming evidence that, on average, nursing mothers lose bone mineral.

17.43 (a) We test H_0: $\mu = 0$ vs. H_a: $\mu > 0$, where μ is the mean sensitivity difference in the population. **(b)** STATE: Does eye grease have a significant impact on eye sensitivity? PLAN: We test the hypotheses stated in part (a). SOLVE: The mean of the 16 differences is $\bar{x} =$ 0.10125, so the test statistic is $z = \dfrac{0.10125 - 0}{0.22/\sqrt{16}} = 1.84$. The one-sided *P*-value for this value of z is $P = 0.0329$. CONCLUDE: The sample gives significant evidence (at $\alpha = 0.05$) that eye grease increases sensitivity.

17.45 (a) No, because 33 falls in the 95% confidence interval, which is (27.5, 33.9). **(b)** Yes, because 34 does not fall in the 95% confidence interval.

17.47 is a Web-based exercise.

Chapter 18 – Inference in Practice

18.1 The most important reason is (c); this is a convenience sample consisting of the first 20 students on a list. This is not an SRS. Anything we learn from this sample will not extend to the larger population. The other two reasons are valid, but less important issues. Reason (a)—the size of the sample and large margin of error—would make the interval less informative, even if the sample were representative of the population. Reason (b)—nonresponse—is a potential problem with every survey, but there is no particular reason to believe it is more likely in this situation.

18.3 Any number of things could go wrong with this convenience sample. The day after Thanksgiving is widely regarded (rightly or wrongly) as a day on which retailers offer great deals—and the kinds of shoppers found that day probably don't represent shoppers generally. Also, the sample isn't random.

18.5 You cannot conclude this. The restaurant you work at is most likely different in many ways from the one where the experiment took place. We cannot talk about 95% of individual days from this confidence interval; the confidence interval is for the average tip, not how many days one might get that average tip.

18.7 The only source of error included in the margin of error is that due to random sampling variability, so (c). Errors due to undercoverage (such as sampling only from landline phones) and nonresponse are not included.

18.9 (a) and (b) The results and the curves are shown below. We see that as the sample size increases, the same difference between μ_0 and $\bar{x}$ goes from being not at all significant to highly significant.

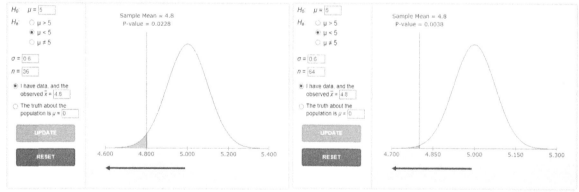

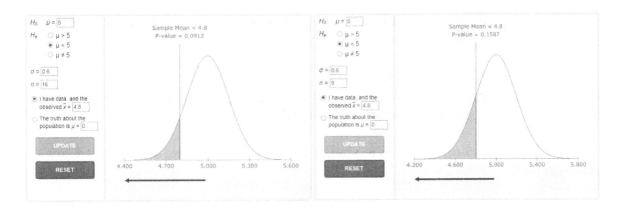

18.11 (a) Each test (subject) has a 5% chance of being deemed "significant" at the 5% level when the null hypothesis (no ESP) is true. With 1000 tests, we'd expect 50 such occurrences. **(b)** Retest the nine promising subjects with a different version of the test.

18.13 For a margin of error ±10, we need at least $n = \left(\dfrac{(1.645)(125)}{10} \right)^2 = 422.82$, so a sample of size 423 will be needed.

18.15 (a) Increase power by taking more measurements. **(b)** If you increase α, you make it easier to reject H_0, thus increasing power. **(c)** A value of $\mu = 260$ is even further from the stated value of $\mu = 243$ under H_0, so power increases.

18.17 The table below summarizes power as σ changes. As σ decreases, power increases. More precise measurements increase the researcher's ability to recognize a false null hypothesis.

σ	55	40	30
Power	0.290	0.442	0.639

18.19 (a) All statistical methods are based on probability samples. We must have a random sample in order to apply them.

18.21 (b) Inference from a voluntary response sample is never reasonable. Online Web surveys are voluntary response surveys.

18.23 (a) There is no control group. Any observed improvement may be due to the treatment, or may be due to another cause.

18.25 (a) The significance level (α) is the probability of rejecting H_0 when H_0 is true.

18.27 (c) Power describes the test's ability to reject a false H_0.

18.29 We need to know that the samples taken from both populations (hunter-gatherers, agricultural) are random. Are the samples large? Recall that if the samples are very large, then even a small, practically insignificant difference in prevalence of color blindness in the two samples will be deemed statistically significant.

18.31 Many people might be reluctant to relate details of their sex lives, or perhaps some will be inclined to exaggerate. It would not be surprising that such an estimate would be biased, but this author cannot guess the direction of bias.

18.33 The effect is greater if the sample is small. With a larger sample, the impact of any one value is small.

18.35 Opinion—even expert opinion—unsupported by data is the weakest type of evidence, so the third description is level C. The second description refers to experiments (clinical trials) and large samples; that is the strongest evidence (level A). The first description is level B: stronger than opinion, but not as strong as experiments with large numbers of subjects.

18.37 (a) The *P*-value decreases (the evidence against H_0 becomes stronger). **(b)** The power increases (the test becomes better at distinguishing between the null and alternative hypotheses).

18.39 (a) The sample mean is $\bar{x} = 9.524$. The test statistic is $z = \dfrac{9.524 - 8}{2/\sqrt{5}} = 1.704$. The *P*-value is $P = 2P(Z \geq 1.704) = 0.0884$ (using software). This is not significant at the 5% level of significance. We would not reject 8 as a plausible value of μ, even though (unknown to the researcher) $\mu = 10$. **(b)** The small sample size makes it difficult to detect a difference that is really there.

   Note: *This is an example of a test with low power; power is an optional topic.*

18.41 (a) "Statistically insignificant" means that the differences observed were no more than might have been expected to occur by chance, even if SES had no effect on LSAT results. **(b)** If the results are based on a small sample, then even if the null hypothesis were not true, the test might not be sensitive enough to detect the effect. Knowing the effects were small tells us that the test was not insignificant merely because of a small sample size.

18.43 $n = \left(\dfrac{(1.96)(3000)}{600}\right)^2 = 96.04$; take $n = 97$.

18.45 (a) This test has a 20% chance of rejecting H_0 when the alternative is true. **(b)** If the test has 20% power, then when the alternative is true, it will fail to reject H_0 80% of the time. **(c)** The sample sizes are very small, which typically leads to low-power tests.

18.47 From the applet, against the alternative $\mu = 10$, power = 0.609.

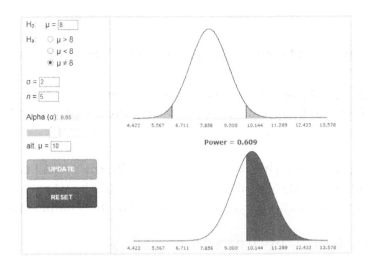

18.49 (a) Because the alternative is $\mu \neq 8$, we reject H_0 at the 5% level when $z \geq 1.96$ or $z \leq -1.96$. **(b)** Here, $z = \dfrac{\bar{x} - 8}{2/\sqrt{5}} = 1.118(\bar{x} - 8)$. We reject H_0 if $1.118(\bar{x} - 8) \leq -1.96$ or if $1.118(\bar{x} - 8) \geq 1.96$. Equivalently (solving for $\bar{x}$), we reject H_0 if $\bar{x} \leq 6.247$ or $\bar{x} \geq 9.753$. **(c)** When $\mu = 10$, the power is $P(\bar{x} \leq 6.247) + P(\bar{x} \geq 9.753) = P\left(Z \leq \dfrac{6.247 - 10}{2/\sqrt{5}}\right) + $

$P\left(Z \geq \dfrac{9.753 - 10}{2/\sqrt{5}}\right) = P(Z \leq -4.20) + P(Z \geq -0.28) = 0.0000 + 0.6103 = 0.6103.$

18.51 Power $= 1 - P(\text{Type II error}) = 1 - 0.36 = 0.64$

18.53 (a) In the long run, this probability should be 0.05. Out of 100 simulated tests, the number of false rejections will have a binomial distribution with $n = 100$ and $P = 0.05$. Most students will see between 0 and 10 rejections. **(b)** If the power is 0.812, the probability of a Type II error is 0.188. Out of 100 simulated tests, the number of false nonrejections will have a binomial distribution with $n = 100$ and $P = 0.188$. Most students will see between 10 and 29 nonrejections. One rejection result is shown below.

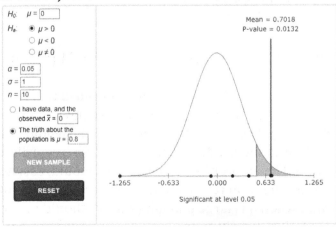

18.55 is a Web-based exercise.

Chapter 19 – From Data Production to Inference: Part III Review

Test Yourself Exercise Answers are answers or sketches. All of these problems are similar to ones found in Chapters 12–18, for which the solutions in this manual provide more detail.

19.1 (a) S = {Male, Female}. **(b)** S = {6, 7, 8, … , 19, 20}. **(c)** S = {All values $2.5 \leq$ VOP ≤ 6.1 liters per minute}. **(d)** S = {All heart rates such that heart rate > 0 bpm}; (students may have other choices for the minimum in this sample space).

19.3 (a) $1 - 0.68 - 0.18 - 0.10 - 0.02 = 0.02$

19.5 $Y > 1$, or $Y \geq 2$; $P(Y \geq 2) = 1 - 0.27 = 0.73$

19.7 (d) $1 - 0.34 = 0.66$

19.9 $P(X \leq 2)$ is the probability of randomly choosing a woman between the ages of 15 and 44 who has given birth to two or fewer children. $P(X \leq 2) = 0.471 + 0.169 + 0.204 = 0.844$ (84.4% of women between the ages of 15 and 44 have given birth to two or fewer children).

19.11 $P(X \geq 3) = 0.104 + 0.034 + 0.018 = 0.156$

19.13 (a) The height of the density curve is $1/5 = 0.2$, because the area under the density function must be 1. See the graph for Exercise 19.14.

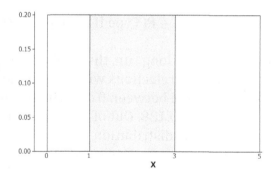

19.15 There is no area above $X = 5$ (the rectangle stops at 5), so $P(4 < X < 7) = P(4 < X \leq 5) = 1/5 = 0.2$.

19.17 (c) mean = 100, standard deviation = $15/\sqrt{60}$ = 1.94 (rounded)

19.19 The answer in Exercise 19.16 would change because this refers to the population distribution, which is now non-Normal (we most likely could not determine this probability). The answer in Exercise 19.17 would not change—the mean of $\bar{x}$ is 100, and the standard deviation of $\bar{x}$ is 1.94, regardless of the population distribution. The answer in Exercise 19.18 would, essentially, not change. The central limit theorem tells us that the sampling distribution of $\bar{x}$ is approximately Normal when n is large enough (and 60 should be large enough), no matter what the population distribution.

19.21 If the population from which we're sampling is heavily skewed, then a larger sample is required for the central limit theorem to apply. If $n = 15$, the sampling distribution of $\bar{x}$ may not be approximately Normal, but if $n = 150$, it will surely be approximately Normal.

19.23 (c) $357 \pm 1.96 \dfrac{50}{\sqrt{8}} = 322.35$ to 391.65

19.25 $357 \pm 1.282 \dfrac{50}{\sqrt{8}} = 334.34$ to 379.66

19.27 (b) $172 \pm 1.645 \dfrac{41}{\sqrt{14}} = 172 \pm 18.03$ mg/dl.

19.29 (c) $n \geq \left(\dfrac{(1.645)(41)}{5} \right)^2 = 181.95$, which rounds up to 182.

19.31 (c) We want to know if your college differed. Remember, hypotheses are in terms of population parameters, not sample statistics.

19.33 (c) $\alpha = 0.10$ but not at $\alpha = 0.05$. The *P*-value is 0.0721.

19.35 (d) $z = \dfrac{357 - 100}{50 / \sqrt{8}} = 14.538$. The actual *P*-value is essentially 0.

19.37 We test $H_0 : \mu = 100$ vs. $H_a : \mu < 100$; $z = \dfrac{87.6 - 100}{15 / \sqrt{113}} = -8.79$; *P*-value ≈ 0. This is overwhelming evidence that the mean IQ for the very-low-birth-weight population is less than 100.

19.39 $P = 0.74$ means that the observed difference is easily explained by random chance (if there is actually no difference, we have a 74% chance of seeing the observed or a larger difference in cholesterol). $P = 0.013$ means that the observed difference was unlikely to have occurred by chance alone; such a result (or something more extreme) would be expected only 13 times in 1000 repetitions of this study.

19.41 (b) This is a personal probability. It is Byron's opinion, and not something based on many repetitions of a football season (which would be impossible).

19.43 (b) $P(\text{over 25 or local}) = P(\text{over 25}) + P(\text{local}) - P(\text{over 25 and local}) = 0.7 + 0.25 - 0.05 = 0.90$

19.45 (b) $P(\text{over 25} \mid \text{not local}) = P(\text{over 25 and not local})/P(\text{not local}) = 0.65/0.75 = 0.867$

19.47 (a) This is binomial, with $n = 5$ and $p = 0.4$.

19.49 $P(X < 600) = P(X \leq 599) = P(Z < -1.37) = 0.0853$

Supplementary Exercises

19.51 (a) All probabilities are between 0 and 1, and their sum is 1. **(b)** Let R_1 be Taster 1's rating and R_2 be Taster 2's rating. Add the probabilities on the diagonal (upper left to lower right): $P(R_1 = R_2) = 0.05 + 0.08 + 0.25 + 0.18 + 0.08 = 0.64$. **(c)** $P(R_1 > R_2) = 0.18$. This is the sum of the ten numbers in the "lower left" part of the table: the bottom four numbers from the first column, the bottom three from the second column, the bottom two from the third column, and the last number in the fourth column. These entries correspond to, for example, "Taster 2 gives a rating of 1, and Taster 1 gives a rating more than 1." $P(R_2 > R_1) = 0.18$; this is the sum of the ten numbers in the "upper right" part of the table. We could also find this by noting that this probability and the other two in this exercise must add to 1 (because they account for all of the entries in the table).

19.53 (a) Out of 100 seniors, nearly all should be in the range $\mu \pm 3\sigma = 3.3 \pm 3(0.8) = 0.9$ to 5.7. **(b)** The sample mean $\bar{x}$ has an $N(\mu, \sigma/\sqrt{100}) = N(3.3, 0.08)$ distribution, so nearly all such means should be in the range $3.3 \pm 3(0.08) = 3.3 \pm 0.24$, or 3.06 to 3.54.

19.55 (a) The stemplot confirms the description given in the text. (Arguably, there are two "mild outliers" visible in the stemplot, although the $1.5 \times IQR$ criterion only flags the highest as an outlier.) **(b)** STATE: Is there evidence that the mean body temperature for all healthy adults is not equal to $98.6°$? PLAN: Let μ be the mean body temperature. We test $H_0: \mu = 98.6°$ vs. $H_a: \mu \neq 98.6°$; the alternative is two-sided because we had no suspicion (before looking at the data) that μ might be higher or lower than $98.6°$. SOLVE: Assume we have a Normal distribution and an SRS. The average body temperature in our sample is $\bar{x} = 98.203°$, so the test statistic is $z = \dfrac{98.203 - 98.6}{0.7/\sqrt{20}} = -2.54$. The two-sided P-value is $P = 2P(Z < -2.54) = 0.0110$. CONCLUDE: We have fairly strong evidence—significant at $\alpha = 0.05$, but not at $\alpha = 0.01$—that mean body temperature is not equal to $98.6°$. (Specifically, the data suggests that mean body temperature is lower.)

96	8
97	344
97	888889
98	0133
98	5789
99	
99	6
100	2

19.57 STATE: What is the mean body temperature μ for healthy adults? PLAN: We will estimate μ by giving a 90% confidence interval. SOLVE: Assume we have a Normal distribution and an SRS. With $\bar{x} = 98.203$, our 90% confidence interval for μ is $98.203 \pm 1.645\left(\dfrac{0.7}{\sqrt{20}}\right) = 98.203 \pm 0.257$, or $97.95°$ to $98.46°$. CONCLUDE: We are

90% confident that the mean body temperature for healthy adults is between 97.95° and 98.46°.

19.59 For the two-sided test $H_0: M = \$50{,}000$ vs. $H_a: M \neq \$50{,}000$ with significance level $\alpha = 0.10$, we can reject H_0 because \$50,000 falls outside the 90% confidence interval.

19.61 Let H be the event student was home schooled. Let R be the event student attended a regular public school. We want $P(H \mid \text{not } R)$. Note that the event "H and not R" = "H." Then $P(H \mid \text{not } R) = \dfrac{P(H)}{P(\text{not } R)} = \dfrac{0.006}{1 - 0.758} = 0.025$.

19.63 (a) For $n = 12$ such users, the distribution of those who have visited an auction site n the past month is binomial with $n = 12$ and $p = 0.50$. $P(X = 8) = \dbinom{12}{8}(0.5)^8(1 - 0.5)^{12-8} = 0.1208$. **(b)** With $n = 500$, the distribution of those who have visited online auction sites will be approximately Normal because $np = n(1 - p) = 500(0.5) = 250$, which is at least 10. The standard deviation is $\sigma = \sqrt{500(0.5)(1 - 0.5)} = 11.18$. $P(X \geq 235) = P(Z \geq -1.34) = 0.9099$.

19.65 A Type I error means that we conclude the mean IQ is less than 100 when it really is 100 (or more). A Type II error means that we conclude the mean IQ is 100 (or more) when it really is less than 100.

Chapter 20 – Inference about a Population Mean

20.1 The standard error of the mean is $s/\sqrt{n} = 56.9/\sqrt{1000} = 1.7993$ minutes.

20.3 (a) $t^* = 2.353$ **(b)** $t^* = 2.485$

20.5 (a) df = 12 – 1 = 11, so $t^* = 2.201$. **(b)** df = 2 – 1 = 1, so $t^* = 63.657$. **(c)** df = 1001 – 1 = 1000, so $t^* = 1.646$.

20.7 STATE: What is the mean percent μ of the number of correct answers when people are told to identify the taller of two speakers by voice? PLAN: We will estimate μ with a 99% confidence interval. SOLVE: We are told to view the observations as an SRS. A stemplot shows some possible bimodality, but no outliers. With $\bar{x}$ = 62.1667% and $s = 5.806\%$ correct, and $t^* = 2.807$ (df = 23), the

```
4 | 9
5 | 3
5 | 6668889
6 | 1123
6 | 556777889
7 | 00
```

99% confidence interval for μ is $62.1667 \pm 2.807\dfrac{5.806}{\sqrt{24}} = 62.1667 \pm 3.3267 = 58.84\%$

to 65.49%. CONCLUDE: We are 99% confident that the mean percent of correct answers to identifying the taller of two people by voice is between 58.84% and 65.49%.

20.9 (a) df = 5 – 1 = 4 **(b)** $t = 2.50$ is bracketed by $t^* = 2.132$ (with two-tail probability 0.10) and $t^* = 2.776$ (with two-tail probability 0.05). Since this is a two-sided significance test, $0.05 < P < 0.10$. **(c)** This test is significant at the 10% level since $P < 0.10$. It is not significant at either the 5% or 1% levels since $P > 0.05$. **(d)** From software, $P = 0.0668$.

20.11 PLAN: Take μ to be the mean difference (with eye grease minus without) in sensitivity. We test $H_0: \mu = 0$ versus $H_a: \mu > 0$, using a one-sided alternative because if the eye grease works, it should increase sensitivity. SOLVE: We must assume that the athletes in the experiment can be regarded as an SRS of all such athletes and that the treatments were randomized. For each athlete, we were provided the difference; a stemplot of these differences (provided) seems to show two outliers; checking with the $1.5 \times IQR$ rule, these are not outliers ($Q_1 = -8$, $Q_3 = 26$, and the upper fence is 77). However, P-values will only be approximate due to the skew and relatively small sample size. The mean and

```
-1 | 8621
-0 | 5
 0 | 23557
 1 | 4
 2 | 489
 3 |
 4 | 3
 5 |
 6 | 4
```

standard deviation are $\bar{x} = 0.1012$ and $s = 0.2263$, so $t = \dfrac{0.1012 - 0}{0.2263/\sqrt{16}} = 1.79$ with df =

15. Using Table C, $P < 0.05$ (software gives 0.0469). CONCLUDE: We have evidence that eye grease does increase sensitivity to contrast. Due to the skew in the data, we may not want to place much emphasis on this result.

20.13 The stemplot suggests that the distribution of nitrogen contents is heavily skewed with a strong outlier. Although *t* procedures are robust, they should not be used if the population being sampled is this heavily skewed. In this case, *t* procedures are not reliable.

```
0 | 00000000000111
0 | 2222233
0 | 44
0 |
0 |
1 |
1 |
1 | 4
```

20.15 (a) The estimate of the standard error from the sample is $\text{SE} = 1.2 / \sqrt{10} = 0.379$. **(b)** Using Minitab, create a command file with a .MTB extension using a text editor such as Notepad. This author's commands are shown below.

random 10 c2;
Normal 0.3 1.2.
let c3(k1)=mean(c2)
let k1=k1+1

Minitab uses k# variables as constants. Here, that is used as an index to keep track of the samples. Initialize that variable using the following command at the MTB> prompt:
MTB> Let k1=1

Now, run the command file using **File, Other Files, Run an Exec**. Input the number of executions, and then find your command file using Select **File**. The command set will then be executed the number of times specified (here, 1000).

From descriptive statistics on the randomization distribution, the standard deviation of the 1000 random sample means is 0.3861; this is our estimate of the standard error, which is close to the value from the usual formula.

Descriptive Statistics: C3

```
Variable    N N*   Mean SE Mean   StDev
C3       1000   0 0.3149  0.0122 0.3861
```

20.17 (b) We virtually never know the value of σ.

20.19 (c) df = 16 – 1 = 15

20.21 (b) 1.476. Here, df = 5.

20.23 (a) \$38,808 to \$51,192. The interval is computed as $45,000 \pm 2.064 \dfrac{15,000}{\sqrt{25}}$.

20.25 (b) If you sample 225 unmarried male students, and then sample 225 unmarried female students, no matching is present.

20.27 For the student group: $t = \dfrac{0.08 - 0}{0.37 / \sqrt{12}} = 0.749$ (not 0.49, as stated). For the nonstudent group: $t = \dfrac{0.35 - 0}{0.37 / \sqrt{12}} = 3.277$ (instead of 3.25, a difference that might be due to rounding error). From Table C, the first P-value (assuming a two-sided alternate hypothesis) is between 0.4 and 0.5 (software gives 0.47), and the second P-value is between 0.005 and 0.01 (software gives 0.007).

20.29 (a) The sample size is very large, so the only potential hazard is extreme skewness. Because scores range only from 0 to 500, there is a limit to how skewed the distribution could be. **(b)** From Table C, we take $t^* = 2.581$ (df = 1000); or using software, take $t^* = 2.579$. For either value of t^*, the 99% confidence interval is 248 ± $t^*(1) = 245.4$ to 250.6, when rounded to one decimal place. **(c)** Because the 99% confidence interval for μ does not contain 243 and is entirely above 243, we can believe the mean for all Dallas children is above basic (above 243).

20.31 (a) A subject's responses to the two treatments would not be independent. Some people react more to medications than others. **(b)** This is a two-sided test because the placebo could stimulate activity or suppress activity at this point in the brain. We have $t = \dfrac{-0.326 - 0}{0.181 / \sqrt{6}} = -4.41$. With df = 5, $P = 0.0069$, there is significant evidence of a difference.

20.33 (a) A stemplot is provided, and it suggests the presence of outliers. The sample is small and the stemplot is skewed, so use of t procedures is not appropriate. **(b)** We will compute two confidence intervals, as called for. In the first interval, using all nine observations, we have df = 8 and $t^* = 1.860$. For the second interval, removing the two outliers (1.15 and 1.35), df = 6 and $t^* = 1.943$. The two 90% confidence intervals are

2	5
3	3358
4	00
5	
6	
7	
8	
9	
10	
11	5
12	
13	5

$$0.549 \pm 1.860\left(\frac{0.403}{\sqrt{9}}\right) = 0.299 \text{ to } 0.799 \text{ grams, and}$$

$$0.349 \pm 1.943\left(\frac{0.053}{\sqrt{7}}\right) = 0.310 \text{ to } 0.388 \text{ grams.}$$

(c) The confidence interval computed without the two outliers is much narrower and has a much lower center. Using fewer data values reduces degrees of freedom (yielding a larger value of t^*). Typically, smaller sample sizes yield larger margins of error. However, both of these effects are offset by removing two values far from the others, and s reduces from 0.403 to 0.053.

20.35 (a) The stemplot provided clearly shows the high outlier mentioned in the text. **(b)** Let μ be the mean difference (control minus experimental) in healing rates. We test $H_0 : \mu = 0$ versus $H_a : \mu > 0$. The alternative hypothesis says that the control limb heals faster; that is, the healing rate is greater for the control limb than for the experimental limb. With all 12 differences: $\bar{x} = 6.417$ and $s = 10.7065$, so $t = \dfrac{6.417 - 0}{10.7065 / \sqrt{12}} = 2.08$.

```
-1 | 3
-0 | 6
-0 |
 0 | 12
 0 | 5789
 1 | 012
 1 |
 2 |
 2 |
 3 | 1
```

With df = 11, $P = 0.0311$ (using software). Omitting the outlier: $\bar{x} = 4.182$ and $s = 7.7565$, so $t = \dfrac{4.182 - 0}{7.7565 / \sqrt{11}} = 1.79$. With df = 10, $P = 0.0520$.

Hence, with all 12 differences, there is greater evidence that the mean healing time is greater for the control limb. When we omit the outlier, the evidence is weaker.

20.37 (a) A histogram of the sample is provided. The sample has a significant outlier, and indicates skew. We might consider applying t procedures to the sample after removing the most extreme observation (37,786). **(b)** If we remove the largest observation, the remaining sample is not heavily skewed and has no outliers. Now, we test $H_0 : \mu = 7000$ versus $H_a : \mu \neq 7000$. With the outlier removed, $\bar{x} = 11,555.16$ and $s = 6,095.015$. Hence,

$t = \dfrac{11,555.16 - 7000}{6095.015 / \sqrt{19}} = 3.258$. With df = 18

(with software), $P = 0.0044$ (this is a two-sided test). There is overwhelming evidence that the mean number of words per day of men at this university differs from 7000 (the sample mean indicates they speak more than 7000 words per day).

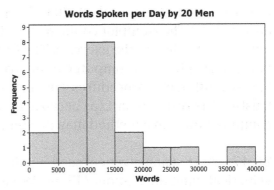

20.39 (a) Each patient was measured before and after treatment. **(b)** The stemplot of differences shows an extreme right-skew, and one or two high outliers. The t procedures should not be used. **(b)** Some students might perform the test ($H_0 : \mu = 0$ versus $H_a : \mu > 0$) using t procedures, despite the presence of strong skew and outliers in the sample. If so, they should find $\bar{x} = 156.36$, $s = 234.2952$, and $t = 2.213$, yielding $P = 0.0256$.

```
0 | 0012238
1 | 0
2 | 1
3 |
4 |
5 | 1
6 |
7 | 0
```

20.41 (a) We test $H_0 : \mu = 0$ versus $H_a : \mu > 0$, where μ is the mean difference (treated − control). This is a one-sided test because the researchers have reason to believe that CO_2 will increase growth rate. **(b)** We have $\bar{x} = 1.916$ and $s = 1.050$, so

$t = \dfrac{1.916 - 0}{1.050 / \sqrt{3}} = 3.16$ with df = 2. $P = 0.0436$. This is significant at the 5% significance

level. **(c)** For very small samples, t procedures should only be used when we can assume that the population is Normal. We have no way to assess the Normality of the population based on these three observations. Thus, the validity of the analysis in (b) is dubious.

20.43 The stemplot (not asked for) reveals that these data contain two extreme high outliers (5973 and 8015). Hence, *t* procedures are not appropriate.

0	1123788
1	00115677899
2	01112458
3	
4	
5	9
6	
7	
8	0

20.45 (a) The mean and standard deviation are $\bar{x}$ = 48.25, and s = 40.24 thousand barrels. From Table C, t^* = 2.000 (df = 60). Using software, with df = 63, t^* = 1.998. The 95% confidence interval for μ is 48.25 ±

$$2.000\left(\frac{40.24}{\sqrt{64}}\right) = 48.25 \pm 10.06 = 38.19 \text{ to } 58.31$$

thousand barrels. (Using software, the confidence interval is almost identical: 38.20 to 58.30 thousand barrels.) **(b)** The stemplot confirms the skewness and

0	00001111111111
0	2222222333333333333
0	44444445555555
0	6666667
0	8899
1	01
1	
1	5
1	
1	9
2	0

outliers described in the exercise. The two intervals have similar widths, but the new interval (using a computer-intensive method) is shifted higher by about 2000 barrels. Although *t* procedures are fairly robust, we should be cautious about trusting the result in part (a) because of the strong skew and outliers. The computer-intensive method may produce a more reliable interval.

20.47 STATE: Can velvetleaf seed beetles be helpful in controlling the velvetleaf plant infestations? PLAN: We will construct a 90% confidence interval for μ, the mean percent of beetle-infected seeds. SOLVE: A stemplot shows a single-peaked and roughly symmetric distribution. We assume that the 28 plants can be viewed as an SRS of the population, so *t* procedures are appropriate. We have $\bar{x}$ = 4.0786 and s = 2.0135%. Using df = 27, the 90% confidence interval for μ is

0	07
1	9
2	24689
3	666778
4	0000336
5	157
6	
7	00
8	57

$$4.0786 \pm 1.703\left(\frac{2.0135}{\sqrt{28}}\right) = 4.0786 \pm 0.648 = 3.43\% \text{ to } 4.73\%.$$

CONCLUDE: The beetle infects less than 5% of seeds, so it is unlikely to be effective in controlling velvetleaf.

20.49 From Exercise 20.48, we have $\bar{x}$ = 0.5283, s = 0.4574, and df = 5. A 95% confidence interval for the mean difference in T cell counts after 20 days on

blinatumomab is $0.5283 \pm 2.571\left(\frac{0.4574}{\sqrt{6}}\right) = 0.5283 \pm 0.4801 = 0.0482$ to 1.0084

thousand cells.

20.51 (a) For each subject, randomly select which knob (right or left) that subject should use first. **(b)** STATE: Do right-handed people find right-handed threads easier to use? PLAN: We test $H_0 : \mu = 0$ versus $H_a : \mu < 0$, where μ denotes the mean difference in time (right-thread time – left-thread time), so that $\mu < 0$ means "right-hand time is less than left-hand time on average." SOLVE: A stemplot of the differences gives no reason that t procedures are not appropriate. We assume our sample can be viewed as an SRS. We have $\bar{x} = -13.32$ seconds and $s = 22.936$ seconds, so $t = \dfrac{-13.32 - 0}{22.936 / \sqrt{25}} = -2.90$. With df = 24 we find $P =$

```
 7 | 688
 8 | 47
 9 | 3
10 | 13578
11 | 256
12 | 33
13 | 357
14 | 5678
15 |
16 | 6
17 | 0
```

0.0039. CONCLUDE: We have good evidence (significant at the 1% level) that the mean difference really is negative—that is, the mean time for right-hand-thread knobs is less than the mean time for left-hand-thread knobs.

20.53 Refer to the solution in Exercise 20.51. With df = 24, $t^* = 1.711$, so the confidence interval for μ is given by $-13.32 \pm 1.711 \left(\dfrac{22.936}{\sqrt{25}} \right) = -13.32 \pm 7.85 = -21.2$ to -5.5 seconds. $\bar{x}_{RH}/\bar{x}_{LH} = 104.12/117.44 = 0.887$. Right-handers working with right-handed knobs can accomplish the task in about 89% of the time needed by those working with left-handed knobs.

20.55 (a) Starting with Table C values, for 90% confidence, $t(100) = 1.660$ and $z^* = 1.645$. For 95% confidence, $t(100) = 1.984$ and $z^* = 1.96$. Similarly, for 99% confidence, $t(100) = 2.626$ and $z^* = 2.576$. The differences are 0.015, 0.024, and 0.05. Larger confidence levels will need more observations. We note that $t(1000)$ is within 0.01 of z^* for all these confidence levels. Using software, we find that $t(150) = 1.655$ for 90% confidence, $t(240) = 1.9699$ for 95% confidence, and $t(485) = 2.586$ for 99.5% confidence. **(b)** Answers will vary. We'll note that the effect of the standard deviation difference multiplies the margin of error in the calculation by 100, which implies that "similar" takes more observations with $\sigma = 100$ than for $\sigma = 1$. Using $n = 485$ with $\sigma = 100$, the 99% t margin of error is 11.74, compared with a 99% z margin of error of 11.69. Using $\sigma = 1$, the margins of error are both 0.117, rounding to three decimal places.

20.57 is a Web-based exercise.

Chapter 21 – Comparing Two Means

21.1 This is a matched pairs design. Each plot is a matched pair.

21.3 This involves a single sample.

21.5 STATE: Does playing with a Nintendo Wii™ improve the laparoscopic abilities of medical students? PLAN: We test $H_0 : \mu_{Wii} = \mu_{NoWii}$ versus $H_a : \mu_{Wii} > \mu_{NoWii}$, where μ_{Wii} is the mean improvement time to perform a virtual gall bladder operation for those who used the Wii™, and μ_{NoWii} is the mean improvement time for those who did not use the Wii™. We use a one-sided alternative because movements with the Wii™ are

```
   Wii  |    | No Wii
        | -0 | 8
   111  | -0 | 21
        |  0 | 223444
877775  |  0 | 566678899
 43322  |  1 | 14
     8  |  1 |
  4421  |  2 | 2
     9  |  2 |
     3  |  3 |
```

similar to those needed to perform the surgery, so practice with the Wii™ should result in more improvement than just performing the same operation again. SOLVE: These data came from participants in a randomized experiment, so the two groups are independent. Stemplots suggest some deviation from Normality and a possible high outlier for the No Wii™ group. Boxplots (not shown) indicate no outliers and a relatively symmetric distribution for the Wii™ group, but both the –88 and 229 are outliers for the No Wii™ group. We proceed with the t test for two samples appealing to robustness (especially good with equal sample sizes). With $\bar{x}_{Wii} =$ 132.71, $\bar{x}_{NoWii} = 59.67$, $s_{Wii} = 98.44$, $s_2 = 63.04$, $n_{Wii} = 21$, and $n_{NoWii} = 21$, SE =

$$\sqrt{\frac{s_1^2}{n_1} + \frac{s_2^2}{n_2}} = 25.509 \text{ and } t = \frac{\bar{x}_1 - \bar{x}_2}{SE} = 2.86.$$ Using df as the smaller of 21 – 1 and 21 – 1, we have df = 20, and $0.0025 < P < 0.005$. Using software, df = 34.04 and $P = 0.0036$. CONCLUDE: There is very strong evidence that playing with a Nintendo Wii™ does help improve the skills of student doctors, at least in terms of the mean time to complete a virtual gall bladder operation.

21.7 From Exercise 21.5, we have $\bar{x}_{Wii} = 132.71$, $\bar{x}_{NoWii} = 59.67$, $n_{Wii} = n_{NoWii} = 21$, and SE = 25.509. A 99% confidence interval for the mean difference in improvement in time to complete the virtual gall bladder operation is $\bar{x}_{Wii} - \bar{x}_{NoWii} \pm t^* SE = 73.04 \pm$ 2.845(25.509) = 0.467 to145.613 seconds. Software uses df = 34.04 and gives an interval of 3.45 to 142.65 seconds.

```
  Lean |   | Obese
     9 | 3 |
       | 4 | 1
       | 4 |
     5 | 4 | 44
     6 | 4 | 6
     8 | 4 |
    10 | 5 | 011
    33 | 5 | 23
     5 | 5 |
     6 | 5 | 6
```

21.9 (a) Back-to-back stemplots of the time data are shown below. They appear to be reasonably Normal, and the discussion in the exercise justifies our treating the data as independent SRS's, so we can use the t procedures. We wish to test $H_0 : \mu_1 = \mu_2$ versus $H_a : \mu_1 < \mu_2$, where μ_1 is the population mean time in the restaurant with no scent, and μ_2 is the mean time in the restaurant with a lavender odor. Here, with $\bar{x}_1 = 91.27$, $\bar{x}_2 = 105.700$, $s_1 = 14.930$, $s_2 = 13.105$, $n_1 = 30$, and $n_2 = 30$: SE $= \sqrt{\dfrac{s_1^2}{n_1} + \dfrac{s_2^2}{n_2}} = 3.627$ and $t = \dfrac{\bar{x}_1 - \bar{x}_2}{SE} = -3.98$. Using software, df $= 57.041$ and $P = 0.0001$. Using the more conservative df $= 29$ (lesser of $30 - 1$ and $30 - 1$) and Table C, $P < 0.0005$. There is very strong evidence that customers spend more time on average in the restaurant when the lavender scent is present. **(b)** Back-to-back stemplots of the spending data are shown below. The distributions are skewed and have many gaps. We wish to test $H_0 : \mu_1 = \mu_2$ versus $H_a : \mu_1 < \mu_2$, where μ_1 is the population mean amount spent in the restaurant with no scent, and μ_2 is the mean amount spent in the restaurant with the lavender odor. Here, with $\bar{x}_1 = €17.5133$, $\bar{x}_2 = €21.1233$, $s_1 = €2.3588$, $s_2 = €2.3450$, $n_1 = 30$, and $n_2 = 30$: SE $= \sqrt{\dfrac{s_1^2}{n_1} + \dfrac{s_2^2}{n_2}} = €0.6073$ and $t = \dfrac{\bar{x}_1 - \bar{x}_2}{SE} = -5.94$. Using software, df $= 57.998$ and $P < 0.0001$. Using the more conservative df $= 29$ and Table C, $P < 0.0005$. There is very strong evidence that customers spend more money on average when the lavender scent is present.

```
          Time in restaurant                Amount spent (euros)
    No scent|   |Lavender         No scent   |  |Lavender
          98| 6 |                          9 |12|
         322| 7 |                            |13|
         965| 7 | 6                          |14|
          44| 8 |            99999999999999  |15|
        7765| 8 | 89                         |16|
       32221| 9 | 234                        |17|
          86| 9 | 578         555555555555   |18| 55555555555
          31|10 | 1234                       |19|
        9776|10 | 5566788999             5   |20| 7
            |11 | 4                       9   |21| 5599999999
          85|11 | 6                           |22| 3558
           1|12 | 14                          |23|
            |12 | 69                          |24| 99
            |13 |                         5   |25| 59
            |13 | 7
```

21.11 We have two small samples ($n_1 = n_2 = 4$), so the t procedures are not reliable unless both distributions are Normal.

21.13 Here are the details of the calculations:

$$SE_{Alone} = \frac{0.68}{\sqrt{37}} = 0.1118$$

$$SE_{Friends} = \frac{0.83}{\sqrt{21}} = 0.1811$$

$$SE = \sqrt{SE_{Alone}^2 + SE_{Friends}^2} = 0.21283$$

$$df = \frac{SE^4}{\frac{1}{36}\left(\frac{0.68^2}{37}\right)^2 + \frac{1}{20}\left(\frac{0.83^2}{21}\right)^2} = \frac{0.00205}{0.00005815} = 35.284$$

$$t = \frac{0.29 - (-0.19)}{0.21283} = 2.255$$

21.15 Reading from the software output shown in the statement of Exercise 21.13, we find that there is a significant difference in mean perceived formidability for men alone and with friends ($t = 2.255$, df = 35.3, $P < 0.02$). Because larger scores indicate greater perceived formidability, it appears that foes appear more formidable when alone as opposed to when with friends.

21.17 The observed means are $\bar{x}_1 = 162.825$ and $\bar{x}_9 = 157.6$. The observed difference in means is 5.225. From Figure 21.6, the one-sided *P*-value is about $0.06 + 0.11 + 0.04 + 0.04 = 0.25$. This is not significant at any common level. We have no evidence that an increase in weeds from one per meter to nine per meter decreases the crop yield.

21.19 (a) a two-sample *t* test. We have two independent populations: females and males.

21.21 (b) Confidence levels and *P*-values from the *t* procedures are quite accurate, even if the population distributions are not exactly Normal.

21.23 (b) $\dfrac{15.84 - 9.64}{\sqrt{\dfrac{8.65^2}{21} + \dfrac{3.43^2}{21}}} = 3.05$

21.25 (a) We suspect that younger people use social networks more than older people, so this is a one-sided alternative.

21.27 (a) To test the belief that women talk more than men, we use a one-sided alternative: $H_0 : \mu_F = \mu_M$ versus $H_a : \mu_F > \mu_M$. **(b)–(d)** The small table below provides a summary of *t* statistics, degrees of freedom, and *P*-values for both studies. The two-sample t statistic is computed as $t = \dfrac{\overline{x}_F - \overline{x}_M}{\sqrt{\dfrac{s_F^2}{n_F} + \dfrac{s_M^2}{n_M}}}$, and we take the

conservative approach for computing df as the smaller sample size minus 1.

Study	t	df	Table C values	P-value
1	-0.248	55	$\lvert t \rvert < 0.679$	$P > 0.25$
2	1.507	19	$1.328 < t < 1.729$	$0.05 < P < 0.10$

Note that for Study 1, we reference df = 50 in Table C. **(e)** The first study gives no support to the belief that women talk more than men; the second study gives weak support, and it is significant only at a relatively high significance level (say $\alpha = 0.10$).

21.29 (a) Call group 1 the Stress group, and group 2 the No stress group. Then, because SEM $= s/\sqrt{n}$, we have $s = $ SEM$\sqrt{n}$. $s_1 = 3\sqrt{20} = 13.416$ and $s_2 = 2\sqrt{51} = 14.283$. **(b)** Using conservative Option 2, df = 19 (the lesser of 20 – 1 and 51 – 1). **(c)** We test $H_0 : \mu_1 = \mu_2$ versus $H_a : \mu_1 \neq \mu_2$. With $n_1 = 20$ and $n_2 = 51$, SE $= \sqrt{\dfrac{s_1^2}{n_1} + \dfrac{s_2^2}{n_2}} = $ 3.605, and $t = \dfrac{\overline{x}_1 - \overline{x}_2}{\text{SE}} = \dfrac{26 - 32}{3.605} = -1.664$. With df = 19, using Table C, $0.10 < P < 0.20$. There is little evidence in support of a conclusion that mean weights of rats in stressful environments differ from those of rats without stress.

21.31 (a) We test $H_0 : \mu_{1975} = \mu_{2006}$ versus $H_a : \mu_{1975} > \mu_{2006}$. SE $= \sqrt{\dfrac{0.81^2}{1165} + \dfrac{0.80^2}{2177}} = $ 0.02928, so the two-sample test statistic is $t = \dfrac{3.37 - 3.32}{0.0293} = 1.708$. This is significant at the 5% level: $P = 0.0439$ (df = 2353.38) or $0.025 < P < 0.05$ (df = 1000). There is good evidence that mean job satisfaction decreased from 1975 to 2006. **(b)** The difference is barely significant at the 0.05 level (most likely due to the large sample sizes). Knowing that 1975 had the highest mean job satisfaction score in this time period casts doubt about whether this is actually decreasing. Also, a difference of 0.05 in the means may not be of practical importance.

21.33 Let μ_C be the mean brain size for players who have had concussions, and let μ_{NC} be the mean for those who have not had concussions. We test $H_0 : \mu_C = \mu_{NC}$ versus $H_a : \mu_C \neq \mu_{NC}$. This is a two-sided test, because we simply want to know if there is a difference in mean brain size. SE $= \sqrt{\dfrac{609.3^2}{25} + \dfrac{815.4^2}{25}} = 203.5803$, and

$$t = \frac{5784 - 6489}{203.5803} = -3.463.$$ Using the conservative version for df (Option 2), df = 24, and 0.002 < P < 0.005. Using software, df = 44.43 and P = 0.0012. There is strong evidence that the mean brain size is different for football players who have had concussions as opposed to those who have not had concussions. **(b)** The fact that these were consecutive cases indicates they are not a random sample of all football players who have or have not had concussions. That could weaken or negate the results of the test. We'd need more information about how and why these players were referred to the institute.

21.35 (a) The hypotheses are $H_0 : \mu_1 = \mu_2$ versus $H_a : \mu_1 > \mu_2$, where μ_1 is the mean gain among all coached students, and μ_2 is the mean gain among uncoached students. We find SE = $\sqrt{\dfrac{59^2}{427} + \dfrac{52^2}{2733}} = 3.0235$, and $t = \dfrac{29 - 21}{3.0235} = 2.646$. Using the conservative approach, df = 426 is rounded down to df = 100 in Table C, and we obtain 0.0025 < P < 0.005. Using software, df = 534.45 and P = 0.0042. There is evidence that coached students had a greater average increase than uncoached students. **(b)** The 99% confidence interval is 8 ± t^*(3.0235), where t^* equals 2.626 (using df = 100 with Table C) or 2.585 (df = 534.45, with software). This gives either 0.06 to 15.94 points or 0.184 to 15.816 points, respectively. **(c)** Increasing one's score by 0 to 16 points is not likely to make a difference in being granted admission or scholarships from any colleges.

21.37 (a) Histograms for both data sets are provided below. Neither sample histogram suggests a strong skew or the presence of strong outliers; t procedures are reasonable here. **(b)** Let μ_1 be the mean tip percentage when the forecast is good, and let μ_2 be the mean tip percentage when the forecast is bad. We have $\bar{x}_1 = 22.22$, $\bar{x}_2 = 18.19$, $s_1 = 1.955$, $s_2 = 2.105$, $n_1 = 20$, and $n_2 = 20$. We test $H_0 : \mu_1 = \mu_2$ versus $H_a : \mu_1 \neq \mu_2$. Here, SE = $\sqrt{\dfrac{s_1^2}{n_1} + \dfrac{s_2^2}{n_2}} = 0.642$ and $t = \dfrac{\bar{x}_1 - \bar{x}_2}{\text{SE}} = 6.274$. Using df = 19 (the conservative Option 2) and Table C, we have P < 0.001. Using software, df = 37.8 and P <

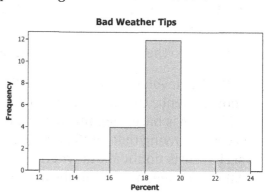

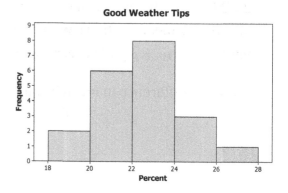

0.00001. There is overwhelming evidence that the mean tip percentage differs between the two types of forecasts presented to patrons.

21.39 Refer to results in Exercise 21.37. Using df = 19, $t^* = 2.093$ and the 95% confidence interval for the difference in mean tip percentages between these two populations is $22.22 - 18.19 \pm 2.093(0.642) = 4.03 \pm 1.34 = 2.69$ to 5.37%. Using df = 37.8 with software, $t^* = 2.025$ and the corresponding 95% confidence interval is 2.73% to 5.33%.

21.41 (a) The mean rating for those with a positive attitude toward Mitt is larger than the mean for those with a negative attitude; the standard deviations are relatively large, however. **(b)** Shown are back-to-back stemplots for the two groups. The distribution of ratings for those with positive attitudes toward Mitt is somewhat right-skewed (but not extremely so). The distribution of ratings for those with negative attitudes toward Mitt is fairly symmetric. A check with a boxplot (not shown) indicates the two lowest are not outliers. **(c)** We find SE =

$$\sqrt{\frac{0.8015^2}{29} + \frac{0.9127^2}{29}} = 0.22556 \text{ and } t = \frac{3.9379 - 3.6103}{0.22556} = 1.452, \text{ for which the } P\text{-value is}$$

$0.10 < P < 0.20$ (using df = 28) or 0.1521 (using software, with df = 55.08). There is no evidence of a difference in the mean trustworthiness rating of Mitt Romney's face, according to whether or not college students had a positive or negative attitude about Mitt (as compared with Barack Obama).

	n	$\overline{x}$	s
Positive	29	3.9379	0.8015
Negative	29	3.6103	0.9127

Positive		Negative
	1	78
	2	
866	2	55569
433220	3	33333
99998776	3	5688999
2211	4	1233334
9766	4	7
300	5	34
7	7	

21.43 (a) Each data value in the stemplot is rounded to the nearest thousand, and stems are in units of ten thousand. So, for example, the row "30 | 2 | 2" represents 3 people: 2 women who spoke about 23,000 and 20,000 words, and 1 man who spoke about 22,000 words. The stemplots suggest that there is some skew in both populations, but the sample sizes should be large enough to overcome this problem. **(b)** With subscripts as assigned in the statement of the problem (Group 1 = Women), we test $H_0 : \mu_1 = \mu_2$ versus $H_a : \mu_1 > \mu_2$. We have $\overline{x}_1 = 16,496.1$, $\overline{x}_2 = 12,866.7$, $s_1 = 7914.35$, $s_2 = 8342.47$,

Women		Men
98876	0	4456789
43321000	1	00111333
998765	1	68
30	2	2
76555	2	8
	3	
	3	8
0	4	

$n_1 = 27$, and $n_2 = 20$; we find SE $= \sqrt{\dfrac{7914.35^2}{27} + \dfrac{8342.47^2}{20}} = 2408.26$, and

$t = \dfrac{16,496.1 - 12,866.7}{2408.26} = 1.51$. With df $= 39.8$ (using software), $P = 0.070$. Using Table C with the more conservative df $= 19$, $0.05 < P < 0.10$. There is some evidence that, on average, women say more words than men, but the evidence is not particularly strong.

21.45 We test $H_0 : \mu_1 = \mu_2$ versus $H_a : \mu_1 \neq \mu_2$, where μ_1 is the mean days behind caterpillar peak for the control group, and μ_2 is the mean days for the supplemented group. Now, with $\bar{x}_1 = 4.0$, $\bar{x}_2 = 11.3$, $s_1 = 3.10934$, $s_2 = 3.92556$, $n_1 = 6$, and $n_2 = 7$, we find SE $= \sqrt{\dfrac{s_1^2}{n_1} + \dfrac{s_2^2}{n_2}} = 1.95263$, and $t = \dfrac{4.0 - 11.3}{\text{SE}} = -3.74$. The two-sided P-value is either $0.01 < P < 0.02$ (using df $= 5$) or 0.0033 (using df $= 10.96$, with software), which agrees with the stated conclusion (a significant difference).

21.47 STATE: Does thinking about money lead people to be more reluctant to ask for help? PLAN: We test $H_0 : \mu_1 = \mu_2$ versus $H_a : \mu_1 > \mu_2$, where μ_1 is the mean time for the treatment group, and μ_2 is the mean time for the control group. The alternative hypothesis is one-sided because the researcher suspects that the treatment group will wait longer before asking for help. SOLVE: We must assume that the data comes from an SRS of the intended population; we cannot check this with the data. The back-to-back stemplot shows some irregularity in the treatment times and skewness in the control times.

Treatment		Control
65	0	5689
3	1	012444
976	1	58
44	2	
5	2	79
	3	
6	3	7
44	4	01
876	4	
3	5	
	5	
0	6	

We hope that our equal and moderately large sample sizes will overcome any deviation from Normality. With $\bar{x}_1 = 314.0588$, $\bar{x}_2 = 186.1176$, $s_1 = 172.7898$, $s_2 = 118.0926$, $n_1 = 17$, and $n_2 = 17$, we find SE $= \sqrt{\dfrac{s_1^2}{n_1} + \dfrac{s_2^2}{n_2}} = 50.7602$, and

$t = \dfrac{314.0588 - 186.1176}{\text{SE}} = 2.521$, for which $0.01 < P < 0.02$ (df $= 16$) or $P = 0.0088$ (df $= 28.27$). CONCLUDE: There is strong evidence that the treatment group waited longer to ask for help on average.

21.49 PLAN: We test $H_0 : \mu_1 = \mu_2$ versus $H_a : \mu_1 < \mu_2$, where μ_1 is the mean change in score for the Active group, and μ_2 is the mean change in score for the Traditional group (if active learning is better, there should be less change in those scores). **SOLVE:** We must assume that the data comes from an SRS of the intended populations. The stemplots for each sample show no heavy skew and no outliers (using the 1.5*IQR* criterion). With $\bar{x}_1 = 3.6$, $\bar{x}_2 = 4.74$, $s_1 = 2.41$, $s_2 = 2.85$, $n_1 = 15$,

Active		Trad.
00	0	0
0	1	00
00	2	000
000	3	000
0	4	0
000	5	000
0	6	0000
0	7	000
0	8	00
	9	
	10	
	11	
	12	0

and $n_2 = 23$. We find SE $= \sqrt{\dfrac{s_1^2}{n_1} + \dfrac{s_2^2}{n_2}} = 0.86$, and $t = \dfrac{3.6 - 4.74}{\text{SE}} = $

-1.32, for which $P = 0.1040$ (14 df). If you use software, df $= 33.42$ and $P = 0.0979$. **CONCLUDE:** There is little support for a conclusion that active learning yields more retention than traditional learning.

21.51 (a) Refer to Exercise 21.49 for details. For 90% confidence, $t^* = 1.761$ (using df $= 14$) or $t^* = 1.692$ (using df $= 33.42$). A 90% confidence interval for $\mu_1 - \mu_2$ is 3.6 $- 4.74 \pm t^*(0.86)$, or -2.65 to 0.37 (using df $= 14$) or -2.60 to 0.32 (using df $= 33.42$). **(b)** Now we want a 90% confidence interval for the mean change in score for the active class. That is, we construct a 90% confidence interval for μ_1. With 15 observations, we have df $= 14$, and $t^* = 1.761$. The confidence interval is given by 3.6 $\pm 1.761 \dfrac{2.41}{\sqrt{15}} = 2.50$ to 4.70.

21.53 Because this exercise asks for a "complete analysis" without suggesting hypotheses or confidence levels, student responses may vary. This solution gives 95% confidence intervals for the means in parts (a) and (b), and performs a hypothesis test and gives a 95% confidence interval for part (c). Note that the first two problems call for single-sample t procedures (Chapter 20), whereas the last uses the Chapter 21 procedures. Student answers should be formatted according to the "four-step process" of the text; these answers are not formatted as such, but can be used to check student results. We begin with summary statistics.

	n	$\bar{x}$	s
Women	95	4.2737	2.1472
Men	81	6.5185	3.3471

A back-to-back stemplot of responses for men and women reveals that the distribution of claimed drinks per day for women is slightly skewed, but has no outliers. For men, the distribution is only slightly skewed but contains four outliers. However, these outliers are not too extreme. In all problems, it seems that the use of t procedures is reasonable.

We construct a 95% confidence interval for μ_w, the mean number of claimed drinks for women. Here, $t^* = 1.990$ (df $= 80$ in Table C) or $t^* = 1.9855$ (df $= 94$, using software), and SE $= 2.1472/\sqrt{95} = 0.2203$. A 95% confidence interval for μ_w is

4.2737 ± 1.990(0.223) = 3.84 to 4.71 drinks. The interval using software is virtually the same. With 95% confidence, the mean number of claimed drinks for women is between 3.84 and 4.71 drinks.

	Women		Men
	00000000	1	000
	5555555500000	2	0000
	5555000000000000000000	3	0000000
	500000000000000000000	4	0000000000555
	00000000000	5	000000005
	50000000	6	00000005
	00000000	7	000000005
	000	8	000000000
	000	9	0000
	00	10	00000005
		11	0
		12	05
		13	
		13	
		15	000
		16	0

(b) We construct a 95% confidence interval for μ_m, the mean number of claimed drinks for men. Here, $t^* = 1.990$ (df = 80 in Table C or using software), and SE = $3.3471/\sqrt{81}$ = 0.3719. A 95% confidence interval for μ_m is 6.5185 ± 1.990(0.3719) = 5.78 to 7.26 drinks. With 95% confidence, the mean number of claimed drinks for men is between 5.78 and 7.26 drinks.

(c) We test $H_0 : \mu_m = \mu_w$ versus $H_a : \mu_m \neq \mu_w$. We have SE = $\sqrt{\dfrac{2.1472^2}{95} + \dfrac{3.3471^2}{81}}$ = 0.4322, and $t = \dfrac{4.2737 - 6.5185}{\text{SE}}$ = −5.193. Regardless of the choice of df (80 or 132.15), this is highly significant ($P < 0.001$). We have very strong evidence that the claimed number of drinks is different for men and women. To construct a 95% confidence interval for $\mu_m - \mu_w$, we use $t^* = 1.990$ (df = 80) or $t^* = 1.9781$ (df = 132.15). Using $\bar{x}_1 - \bar{x}_2 \pm t^* \sqrt{\dfrac{s_1^2}{n_1} + \dfrac{s_2^2}{n_2}}$, we obtain either 2.2448 ± 0.8601 or 2.2448 ± 0.8549. After rounding either interval, we report that with 95% confidence, on average, sophomore men who drink claim an additional 1.4 to 3.1 drinks per day compared with sophomore women who drink.

21.55 is a Web-based exercise.

Chapter 22 – Inference about a Population Proportion

22.1 (a) The population is surgical patients. p is the proportion of all surgical patients who will test positive for *Staphylococcus aureus*. **(b)** $\hat{p} = \dfrac{1251}{6771} = 0.185$, or 18.5%.

22.3 (a) Because $np = 0.90(1500) = 1350$ and $n(1-p) = 0.10(1500) = 150$, and both are at least 10, the sampling distribution of $\hat{p}$ is approximately Normal, with mean $p = 0.90$ and standard deviation $\sqrt{\dfrac{p(1-p)}{n}} = \sqrt{\dfrac{0.90(1-.90)}{1500}} = 0.0077$. **(b)** If $n = 6000$, the sampling distribution of $\hat{p}$ is approximately Normal, with mean $p = 0.90$ and standard deviation $\sqrt{\dfrac{p(1-p)}{n}} = \sqrt{\dfrac{0.90(1-.90)}{6000}} = 0.0039$. Notice that quadrupling the sample size (from 1500 to 6000) results in halving the standard deviation of $\hat{p}$ (0.0039 is one-half of 0.0077, at least to within rounding).

22.5 (a) The survey excludes residents of the northern territories, as well as those who have no phones or have only cell phone service. **(b)** $\hat{p} = \dfrac{1288}{1505} = 0.8558$, so SE $= \sqrt{\dfrac{\hat{p}(1-\hat{p})}{n}} = 0.009055$, and the 95% confidence interval is $0.8558 \pm (1.96)(0.009055) = 0.8381$ to 0.8735, or 83.8% to 87.4%.

22.7 (a) We have $\hat{p} = \dfrac{42}{165} = 0.255$, so the margin of error is $1.96\sqrt{\dfrac{0.255(1-0.255)}{165}} = 0.0665$. **(b)** For a ±3% margin of error, we'll need more than four times this sample size, because 3% is less than half the original margin of error. The actual number needed in the sample (using the original value of $\hat{p}$ as p^*) is

$$n = \left(\dfrac{1.96}{0.03}\right)^2 (0.255)(1-0.255) = 810.898,$$ so we need at least 811 visitors over age 65.

22.9 STATE: We wonder if the proportion of times the Belgian euro coin spins heads is the same as the proportion of times it spins tails. SOLVE: Let p be the proportion of times a spun Belgian euro coin lands heads. We test $H_0 : p = 0.50$ versus $H_a : p \neq 0.50$. Because the sample consists of 250 trials, we expect 125 "successes" (heads) and 125 "failures" (tails); both of these are at least 10, and we assume the sample represents an SRS of all possible coin spins, so the conditions are met. $\hat{p} = \dfrac{140}{250} = 0.56$, and SE $= \sqrt{\dfrac{p_0(1-p_0)}{n}} = \sqrt{\dfrac{0.50(1-0.50)}{250}} = 0.0316$. $z = \dfrac{\hat{p} - p_0}{\text{SE}} = \dfrac{0.56 - 0.50}{0.0316} =$

1.90, and $P = 0.0574$. CONCLUDE: There is some evidence that the proportion of times a Belgian euro coin spins heads is not 0.50; the P-value is close to 0.05, but not less than 0.05. Perhaps more spins would be conclusive.

22.11 (a) The number of trials is not large enough to apply the z test for a proportion. Here, the expected number of successes (heads) and the expected number of failures (tails) are both 5; these should be 10 or more. **(b)** As long as the sample can be viewed as an SRS, a z test for a proportion can be used. **(c)** Under the null hypothesis, we expect only $200(0.01) = 2$ failures. We should have at least 10 expected failures and at least 10 expected successes.

22.13 The large-sample conditions are met because we had 113 people who have experienced computer crime and $1025 - 113 = 912$ people who have not; both are at least 10. **(a)** $\hat{p} = \dfrac{113}{1025} = 0.1102$, and $SE_{\hat{p}} = \sqrt{\dfrac{\hat{p}(1-\hat{p})}{1025}} = 0.0098$. A 95% confidence interval for p is given by $0.1102 \pm 1.96(0.0098) = 0.0910$ to 0.1294, or 9.1% to 12.9%. **(b)** Using the plus four method, $\tilde{p} = \dfrac{113+2}{1025+4} = 0.1118$, and $SE_{\tilde{p}} = \sqrt{\dfrac{\tilde{p}(1-\tilde{p})}{1029}} = 0.0098$. A 95% confidence interval for p is given by $0.1118 \pm 1.96(0.0098) = 0.0926$ to 0.1310, or 9.3% to 13.1%. These intervals are virtually identical, but the plus four confidence interval is very slightly shifted to the right. This shift is very small because adding 2 successes and 2 failures to an already large sample size (1025) has little impact.

22.15 (b) The sampling distribution of $\hat{p}$ has mean $p = 0.60$.

22.17 (b) The 90% confidence interval is $0.80 \pm 1.645\sqrt{\dfrac{0.80(1-0.80)}{4500}}$.

22.19 (c) $n = \left(\dfrac{z^*}{m}\right)^2 p^*\left(1-p^*\right) = \left(\dfrac{2.576}{0.02}\right)^2 (0.5)(0.5) = 4147.36$, so we would need at least 4148.

22.21 (a) Sources of bias are not accounted for in a margin of error.

22.23 (c) The P-value is 0.0057.

22.25 (a) The survey excludes those who have no phones or have only cell phone service. **(b)** Note that we have 848 "Yes" answers and 162 "no" answers; both of these are at least 15. With the sample proportion $\hat{p} = \dfrac{848}{1010} = 0.8396$, the large-sample 95% confidence interval is $0.8396 \pm 1.96 \sqrt{\dfrac{0.8396(1-0.8396)}{1010}} = 0.8170$ to 0.8622.

22.27 (a) With $\hat{p} = \dfrac{848}{1010} = 0.8396$, SE = 0.01155, so the margin of error is $1.96\,\text{SE} = 0.02263 = 2.26\%$. **(b)** If instead $\hat{p} = 0.50$, then SE = 0.01573 and the margin of error for 95% confidence would be $1.96\,\text{SE} = 0.03084 = 3.08\%$. **(c)** For samples of about this size, the margin of error is no more than about $\pm 3\%$, no matter what $\hat{p}$ is.

22.29 (a) The survey excludes residents of Alaska and Hawaii, and those who do not have cell phone service. **(b)** We have 422 successes and 2063 failures (both at least 15), so the sample is large enough to use the large-sample confidence interval. We have $\hat{p} = \dfrac{422}{2485} = 0.1698$, and $\text{SE} = \sqrt{\dfrac{0.1698(1-0.1698)}{2485}} = 0.0075$. For 90% confidence, the margin of error is $1.645\,\text{SE} = 0.0124$ and the confidence interval is 0.1574 to 0.1822, or 15.7% to 18.2%. **(c)** Perhaps people who use the cell phone to search for information online are younger and more interested in sexually related topics.

22.31 (a) Both the large-sample and plus four methods are safe because we have 880 trials, with 171 successes and $880 - 171 = 709$ failures. For the large-sample interval, $\hat{p} = \dfrac{171}{880} = 0.1943$, $\text{SE} = \sqrt{\dfrac{(0.1943)(1-0.1943)}{880}} = 0.01334$, the margin of error is $1.96\,\text{SE} = 0.02614$, and the 95% confidence interval is 0.1682 to 0.2204. **(b)** It is likely that more than 171 respondents have run red lights. We would not expect very many people to claim that they have run red lights when they have not, but some people will deny running red lights when they have.

22.33 (a) The margins of error are $1.96\sqrt{\dfrac{\hat{p}(1-\hat{p})}{100}} = 0.196\sqrt{\hat{p}(1-\hat{p})}$ (shown in the table below). **(b)** With $n = 500$, the margins of error are $1.96\sqrt{\dfrac{\hat{p}(1-\hat{p})}{500}} = 0.088\sqrt{\hat{p}(1-\hat{p})}$. The new margins of error are less than half their former size. Because we have not been given any idea of the value of $\hat{p}$, we used 0.5.

	p	0.1	0.3	0.5	0.7	0.9
(a)	m.e.	0.0588	0.0898	0.0980	0.0898	0.0588
(b)	m.e.	0.0263	0.0402	0.0438	0.0402	0.0263

22.35 PLAN: With p representing the proportion of songs downloaded by Rina, we test $H_0 : p = 0.50$ versus $H_a : p \neq 0.50$. The test is two-sided because we wonder if the proportion downloaded by Rina differs from that downloaded by Ed, which would mean that p differs from 0.5. SOLVE: We assume that the 50 songs sampled are an SRS. With 50 songs sampled, we expect 50(0.50) = 25 successes and 50(0.50) = 25 failures (which are both at least 10), so conditions for use of the large-sample z test are satisfied. We have $\hat{p} = \dfrac{34}{50} = 0.68$, so $\dfrac{0.68-0.50}{\sqrt{\dfrac{0.50(1-0.50)}{50}}} = 2.55$ and $P = 0.0108$.

CONCLUDE: There is strong evidence that the proportion of songs downloaded by Rina differs from 0.50. In fact, it seems that Rina downloaded more than Ed. **(b)** The conditions for a large-sample confidence interval are met because 34 of the sample's 50 songs were downloaded by Rina and 16 by Ed; both of these are larger than 15. The 95% confidence interval for the proportion downloaded by Rina is 0.68 ± $1.96\sqrt{\dfrac{0.68(1-0.68)}{50}} = 0.5507$ to 0.8093. At 95% confidence, Rina has downloaded between about 55% and 81% of the songs on their player.

22.37 (a) The hypotheses are $H_0 : p = 0.15$ and $H_a : p > 0.15$. The chance of obtaining a sample proportion $\hat{p} = \dfrac{15}{61} = 0.2459$ if the true proportion is $p = 0.15$ is 0.0178 (1.78%) because $z = \dfrac{0.2459-0.15}{\sqrt{0.15(1-0.15)/61}} = 2.10$. This type of result (or something even more extreme) would be expected to happen less than once in 50 trials, which is rare. Here, we expect 0.15(61) = 9.15 "successes"; because this is less than 10, there is a possible problem with the use of the z test in this case. Whether we can view this particular class as a simple random sample (of all this teacher's students? of all AP statistics students?) is questionable. **(b)** Answers will vary. This was not a designed, randomized experiment, so we cannot say the cash incentive "caused" the increase in 5's.

22.39 (a) PLAN: We have $H_0 : p = 0.50$ and $H_a : p \neq 0.50$. The alternate is two-sided because we want to know if subjects are *not* equally likely to choose either of the two positions. SOLVE: We assume we have an SRS from the population. With 32 subjects, we expect 16 successes (people who would pick the first wine) and 16 failures (people who would pick the second wine). $\hat{p} = \dfrac{22}{32} = 0.6875$ and $z = \dfrac{0.6875-0.50}{\sqrt{0.50(0.50)/32}} = 2.12$, with P-value 2(0.0170) = 0.0340. CONCLUDE: We have strong evidence that people are not equally likely to choose either of two options (of identical wine). It appears they are more likely to select the first presented wine as their preference. **(b)** People who would go out of their way to participate in such a study are presumed to represent the population of all wine drinkers (or adults). The assumption that we have a simple random sample may not be reasonable.

22.41 PLAN: We obtain the sample size required to estimate the proportion of wine tasters who select the first choice to within ± 0.05 with 95% confidence. SOLVE: We guess that the unknown value of p is 0.6875, as computed in Exercise 22.39. $n =$

$$\left(\frac{z^*}{m}\right)^2 p^*\left(1-p^*\right) = \left(\frac{1.96}{0.05}\right)^2 (0.6875)(1-0.6875) = 330.14, \text{ so take } n = 331.$$

CONCLUDE: We require a sample of at least 331 wine tasters in order to estimate the proportion of tasters who would choose the first option to within 0.05 with 95% confidence.

22.43 PLAN: We will give a 90% confidence interval for the proportion of all *Krameria cytisoides* shrubs that will resprout after a fire. SOLVE: We assume that the 12 shrubs in the sample can be treated as an SRS. Because the number of resprouting shrubs is just 5, the conditions for a large-sample interval are not met.

Using the plus four method: $\tilde{p} = \dfrac{5+2}{12+4} = 0.4375$, SE = 0.1240, the margin of error is 1.645 SE = 0.2040, and the 90% confidence interval is 0.2335 to 0.6415. CONCLUDE: We are 90% confident that the proportion of *Krameria cytisoides* shrubs that will resprout after a fire is between about 0.23 and 0.64.

22.45 is a Web-based exercise.

Chapter 23 – Comparing Two Proportions

23.1 PLAN: Let p_M be the proportion of all males who have used the Internet to search for health information and p_F be the proportion of females who have done so. We want a 95% confidence interval for the difference in these proportions. SOLVE: The samples were large with clearly more than 10 "successes" and "failures" in each sample. The sample proportions are $p_F = \dfrac{811}{1308} = 0.6200$ and

$p_M = \dfrac{520}{1084} = 0.4797$. The standard error of the difference is

$$SE = \sqrt{\frac{0.62(1-0.62)}{1308} + \frac{0.4797(1-0.4797)}{1084}} = 0.0203.$$ The 95% confidence interval is (0.62 – 0.4797) ± 1.96(0.0203) = 0.1403 ± 0.0398, or 0.1005 to 0.1801. CONCLUDE: We are 95% confident that between 10% and 18% more women than men have looked for health information on the Internet.

23.3 PLAN: Let p_1 be the proportion of 18- to 29-year-olds who think claims about the environment are exaggerated and p_2 be the proportion of those 60 and older who think so. We want a 95% confidence interval for the differences in these proportions. SOLVE: The samples were large, with clearly more than 10 "successes" and "failures" in each sample. The sample proportions are $p_2 = \dfrac{174}{376} = 0.4628$ and

$p_1 = \dfrac{75}{251} = 0.2988$. The standard error of the difference is

$$SE = \sqrt{\frac{0.4628(1-0.4628)}{376} + \frac{0.2988(1-0.2988)}{251}} = 0.0387.$$ The 95% confidence interval for the difference in proportions is (0.4628 – 0.2988) ± 1.96(0.0387) = 0.164 ± 0.0759 = 0.0881 to 0.2399. CONCLUDE: Based on these samples, we are 95% confident that between about 8.8% and 24.0% more people 60 and older believe that claims about the environment are exaggerated than people 18 to 29 years old.

23.5 STATE: Is helmet use less common among skiers and snowboarders with head injuries than skiers and snowboarders without head injuries? PLAN: Let p_1 and p_2 be (respectively) the proportions of injured skiers and injured snowboarders who wear helmets. We test $H_0 : p_1 = p_2$ versus $H_a : p_1 < p_2$. SOLVE: The smallest count is 96, so the significance testing procedure is safe. We find $\hat{p}_1 = \dfrac{96}{578} = 0.1661$ and $\hat{p}_2 =$

$\dfrac{656}{2992} = 0.2193$. The pooled proportion is $\hat{p} = \dfrac{96+656}{578+2992} = 0.2106$. Then for the significance test, $SE = \sqrt{\hat{p}(1 - \hat{p})\left(\frac{1}{578} + \frac{1}{2992}\right)} = 0.01853$. The test statistic is

therefore $z = \dfrac{0.1661 - 0.2193}{0.01853} = -2.87$, and $P = 0.0021$. CONCLUDE: We have strong

evidence (significant at $\alpha = 0.01$) that skiers and snowboarders with head injuries are less likely to use helmets than skiers and snowboarders without head injuries.

23.7 (a) One count is only 6, and the guidelines for using the large-sample confidence interval call for all counts to be at least 10. **(b)** For the plus four method, the sample sizes are 55 and 110, and the success counts are 7 and 46. **(c)** We have

$\tilde{p}_1 = \dfrac{6+1}{53+2} = 0.1273$ and $\tilde{p}_2 = \dfrac{45+1}{108+2} = 0.4182$. A plus four 95% confidence interval

for $p_1 - p_2$ is $(0.1273 - 0.4182) \pm 1.96 \sqrt{\dfrac{\tilde{p}_1(1-\tilde{p}_1)}{55} + \dfrac{\tilde{p}_2(1-\tilde{p}_2)}{110}} = -0.2909 \pm 0.1275 =$

-0.4184 to -0.1634. Since the first population is for injured skaters with wrist guards, the proportion for skaters with wrist guards is seen to be lower than the proportion for skaters without wrist guards. With 95% confidence, among injured skaters the difference between proportion with wrist guards and those without is between -41.8% and -16.3%. That is, it appears that more injured skaters fail to wear wrist guards.

23.9 (a) The question is "Is there a difference?"

23.11 (b) $\hat{p} = \dfrac{459 + 552}{573 + 719}$

23.13 (b) The standard error is $\sqrt{\dfrac{0.801(1 - 0.801)}{573} + \dfrac{0.768(1 - 0.768)}{719}} = 0.0229$. The

margin of error is $1.645(0.0229) = 0.0377$.

23.15 (b) We have only three failures in the treatment group and only two successes in the control group.

23.17 (a) The four counts are 117, 53, 152, and 165, so all counts are large enough.
(b) Using the large-sample method, $\hat{p}_1 = \dfrac{117}{170} = 0.6882$, and $\hat{p}_2 = \dfrac{152}{317} = 0.4795$, and the

95% confidence interval is $\hat{p}_1 - \hat{p}_2 \pm 1.96 \sqrt{\dfrac{\hat{p}_1(1 - \hat{p}_1)}{170} + \dfrac{\hat{p}_2(1 - \hat{p}_2)}{317}} = 0.2087 \pm 0.0887 =$

0.1200 to 0.2974. Based on these samples, between 12% and 29.7% more younger teens than older teens have posted false information in their online profiles, at 95% confidence.

23.19 (a) One of the counts is 0; for large-sample methods, we need all counts to be at least 10 for the confidence interval (at least 5 for the hypothesis test). **(b)** After we add the two observations to each sample, the sample size for the treatment group is 35, 24 of which have tumors; the sample size for the control group is 20, 1 of which has a tumor. **(c)** $\tilde{p}_1 = \dfrac{23+1}{33+2} = 0.6857$ and $\tilde{p}_2 = \dfrac{0+1}{18+2} = 0.05$. The plus four 99% confidence interval is

$$\tilde{p}_1 - \tilde{p}_2 \pm 2.576 \sqrt{\frac{\tilde{p}_1(1-\tilde{p}_1)}{35} + \frac{\tilde{p}_2(1-\tilde{p}_2)}{20}} = 0.6357 \pm 0.2380 = 0.3977 \text{ to } 0.8737.$$

We are 99% confident that lowering DNA methylation increases the incidence of tumors by between about 40% and 87%.

23.21 (a) Let p_1 and p_2 be (respectively) the proportions of subjects in the music and no music groups who receive a passing grade on the Maryland HSA. We test $H_0: p_1 = p_2$ versus $H_a: p_1 \neq p_2$. For the music group, $\hat{p}_1 = \dfrac{2818}{3239} = 0.870$. For the no music group, $\hat{p}_2 = \dfrac{2091}{2787} = 0.750$. The pooled estimate is $\hat{p} = \dfrac{2818+2091}{3239+2787} = 0.815$. Hence,

$$z = \frac{\hat{p}_1 - \hat{p}_2}{\sqrt{\hat{p}(1-\hat{p})\left(\dfrac{1}{3239}+\dfrac{1}{2787}\right)}} = 11.94.$$ An observed difference of $0.87 - 0.75 = 0.12$ in group proportions is much too large to be explained by chance alone, and $P < 0.0001$. We have overwhelming evidence (Or do we? See part (b).) that the proportion of music students passing the Maryland HSA is greater than that for the no music group. **(b) and (c)** This is an observational study—people who choose to (or can afford to) take music lessons differ in many ways from those who do not. Hence, we cannot conclude that music causes an improvement in Maryland HSA achievement.

23.23 We have at least 10 successes and 10 failures for both samples. For the music group, $\hat{p}_1 = \dfrac{2818}{3239} = 0.870$. For the no music group, $\hat{p}_2 = \dfrac{2091}{2787} = 0.750$. $\hat{p}_1 - \hat{p}_2 \pm 1.96$

$$\sqrt{\frac{\hat{p}_1(1-\hat{p}_1)}{3239} + \frac{\hat{p}_2(1-\hat{p}_2)}{2787}} = 0.100 \text{ to } 0.140, \text{ or } 10.0\% \text{ to } 14.0\%.$$

23.25 (a) To test $H_0: p_M = p_F$ versus $H_a: p_M \neq p_F$, we find $\hat{p}_M = \dfrac{15}{106} = 0.1415$, $\hat{p}_F = \dfrac{7}{42} = 0.1667$, and $\hat{p} = 0.1486$. Then, SE $= \sqrt{\hat{p}(1-\hat{p})\left(\dfrac{1}{106}+\dfrac{1}{42}\right)} = 0.06485$, so

$$z = \frac{\hat{p}_M - \hat{p}_F}{0.06485} = -0.39.$$ This gives $P = 0.6966$, which provides virtually no evidence of a

difference in failure rates. **(b)** We have $\hat{p}_M = \frac{450}{3180} = 0.1415$, $\hat{p}_F = \frac{210}{1260} = 0.1667$, and

$\hat{p} = 0.1486$, but now SE $= \sqrt{\hat{p}(1-\hat{p})\left(\frac{1}{3180} + \frac{1}{1260}\right)} = 0.01184$, so $z = \frac{\hat{p}_M - \hat{p}_F}{0.01184} = -$

2.13 and $P = 0.0332$. **(c)** We are asked to construct two confidence intervals—one based on the smaller samples of part (a) and one based on the larger samples of part (b). First, for case (a), $\hat{p}_M = 0.1415$ and $\hat{p}_F = 0.1667$, so a 95% confidence interval for the difference is

$$\hat{p}_M - \hat{p}_F \pm 1.96\sqrt{\frac{\hat{p}_M(1-\hat{p}_M)}{106} + \frac{\hat{p}_F(1-\hat{p}_F)}{42}} = -0.156 \text{ to } 0.1056. \text{ We note that because}$$

there were only seven business failures in those businesses headed by women, this interval is not really appropriate (even though the hypothesis test was appropriate). For case (b), $\hat{p}_M = 0.1415$ and $\hat{p}_F = 0.1667$. The resulting confidence interval is

$$\hat{p}_M - \hat{p}_F \pm 1.96\sqrt{\frac{\hat{p}_M(1-\hat{p}_M)}{3180} + \frac{\hat{p}_F(1-\hat{p}_F)}{1260}} = -0.0491 \text{ to } -0.0013.$$

23.27 PLAN: Let p_W be the proportion of whites who use social networking sites and p_H be the proportion of Hispanics who use them. We want to know if the proportions are different, so we will test $H_0 : p_W = p_H$ versus $H_a : p_W \neq p_H$. SOLVE: All sample counts are larger than 10 (the smallest is 43 for Hispanics who do not use social networking sites), so inference is appropriate. The sample proportions are

$\hat{p}_W = \frac{866}{1332} = 0.6502$ and $\hat{p}_H = \frac{111}{154} = 0.7208$. The pooled proportion is

$\hat{p} = \frac{866+111}{1332+154} = 0.6575$. The test statistic is $z = \dfrac{0.6502 - 0.7208}{\sqrt{0.6575(1-0.6575)\left(\dfrac{1}{1332} + \dfrac{1}{154}\right)}} = -1.75$.

The P-value of the test is 0.0801. CONCLUDE: At the 0.05 level, we fail to reject H_0. This survey has failed to find a difference in the proportions of whites and Hispanics who use social networking sites.

23.29 PLAN: We construct a 99% confidence interval for $p_1 - p_2$, where p_1 denotes the proportion of people on Chantix® who abstained from smoking, and p_2 is the corresponding proportion for the placebo population. SOLVE: The sample counts are 155 and 61 (successes for treatment and control groups, respectively) and 197 and 283 (failures for the groups), so the large-sample procedures are safe. Using the

large-sample method, $\hat{p}_1 = \frac{155}{352} = 0.4403$ and $\hat{p}_2 = \frac{61}{344} = 0.1773$, and the 99%

confidence interval is $\hat{p}_1 - \hat{p}_2 \pm 2.576\sqrt{\frac{\hat{p}_1(1-\hat{p}_1)}{352} + \frac{\hat{p}_2(1-\hat{p}_2)}{344}} = 0.2630 \pm 0.0864 =$

0.1766 to 0.3494. CONCLUDE: We are 99% confident that the success rate for abstaining from smoking is between 17.7 and 34.9 percentage points higher for smokers using Chantix® than for smokers on a placebo.

23.31 PLAN: Let p_1 be the proportion of people who will reject an unfair offer from another person and p_2 be the proportion for offers from a computer. We test $H_0 : p_1 = p_2$ versus $H_a : p_1 > p_2$. SOLVE: All counts are greater than 5, so the conditions for a significance test are met. The sample proportions are $\hat{p}_1 = \dfrac{18}{38} = 0.4737$ and $\hat{p}_2 = \dfrac{6}{38} = 0.1579$. The pooled proportion is $\hat{p} = \dfrac{18+6}{38+38} = 0.3158$, and

$SE = \sqrt{\hat{p}(1-\hat{p})\left(\dfrac{1}{38} + \dfrac{1}{38}\right)} = 0.1066$. The test statistic is therefore $z = \dfrac{0.4737 - 0.1579}{0.1066} = 2.96$, for which $P = 0.0015$. CONCLUDE: There is very strong evidence that people are more likely to reject an unfair offer from another person than from a computer.

23.33 PLAN: Let p_1 and p_2 be (respectively) the proportions of mice ready to breed in good acorn years and bad acorn years. We give a 90% confidence interval for $p_1 - p_2$. SOLVE: One count is only 7, and the guidelines for using the large-sample method call for all counts to be at least 10, so we use the plus four method. We have $\tilde{p}_1 = \dfrac{54+1}{72+2} = 0.7432$ and $\tilde{p}_2 = \dfrac{10+1}{17+2} = 0.5789$, so the plus four 90% confidence interval is

$$\tilde{p}_1 - \tilde{p}_2 \pm 1.645\sqrt{\dfrac{\tilde{p}_1(1-\tilde{p}_1)}{74} + \dfrac{\tilde{p}_2(1-\tilde{p}_2)}{19}} = 0.1643 \pm 0.2042 = -0.0399 \text{ to } 0.3685.$$

CONCLUDE: We are 90% confident that the proportion of mice ready to breed in good acorn years is between 0.04 lower than and 0.37 higher than the proportion in bad acorn years.

23.35 (a) This is an experiment because the researchers assigned subjects to the groups being compared. **(b)** PLAN: Let p_1 and p_2 be (respectively) the proportions of subjects who have an RV infection for the HL+ group and the control group. We test $H_0 : p_1 = p_2$ versus $H_a : p_1 < p_2$. SOLVE: We have large-enough counts (49, 67, 49, 47) to use the large-sample significance testing procedure safely. Now, $\hat{p}_1 = \dfrac{49}{49+67} = 0.4224$, $\hat{p}_2 = \dfrac{49}{49+47} = 0.5104$, and $\hat{p} = \dfrac{49+49}{116+96} = 0.4623$. $SE = \sqrt{\hat{p}(1-\hat{p})\left(\dfrac{1}{116} + \dfrac{1}{96}\right)} = 0.0688$. The test statistic is therefore $z = \dfrac{0.4224 - 0.5104}{0.0688} = -1.28$, for which $P = 0.1003$. CONCLUDE: We do not have enough evidence to reject the null hypothesis; there is little evidence to conclude that the proportion of HL+ users with a rhinovirus infection is less than that for non-HL+ users.

23.37 is a Web-based exercise.

Chapter 24 – Inference about Variables: Part IV Review

Test Yourself Exercise Solutions contain only answers or sketches of answers. All of these problems are similar to the ones found in Chapters 20–23, for which the solutions in this manual provide more detail.

24.1 (c) The margin of error is $2.056(9.3)/\sqrt{27} = 3.7$.

24.3 (b) $t = 2.023$, df = 13

24.5 (d) Our estimate is $\hat{p} = 676/1760 = 0.384$.

24.7 (d) The standard error is $SE = \sqrt{\dfrac{0.354(1-0.354)}{1734} + \dfrac{0.384(1-0.384)}{1760}} = 0.0163$.

24.9 (a) The standard error is 0.0171. **(b)** A 95% confidence interval is 0.497 to 0.563.

24.11 (b) $2.33 \pm 1.984\dfrac{1.00}{\sqrt{135}}$, using 100 df from Table C.

24.13 (b) This value is from software.

24.15 The standard deviations are larger than the means. Because PedMIDAS scores must be greater than or equal to 0, the distributions must be right-skewed. The sample sizes are fairly large ($n = 64$ and 71), so the sample means should be approximately Normal by the central limit theorem.

24.17 (b) Use technology.

24.19 (c) We would have to view these children as random samples from the larger population of children who could be in her class.

24.21 (b) $\hat{p} = 225/757 = 0.297$

24.23 (b) $0.297 \pm 1.645(0.017)$

24.25 (c) It seems reasonable that the researchers suspect that VLBW babies are less likely to graduate from high school.

24.27 (b)$z = \dfrac{0.7397 - 0.8283}{\sqrt{\hat{p}(1-\hat{p})\left(\frac{1}{242} + \frac{1}{233}\right)}} = -2.34$

24.29 (d) $t = \dfrac{86.2 - 89.8}{\sqrt{\dfrac{13.4^2}{38} + \dfrac{14^2}{54}}} = -1.25$, and the test is two-sided.

24.31 (b) $= \dfrac{0.379 - 0.41}{\sqrt{0.41(1-0.41)/348}} = -1.18$, so $P = 0.1190$.

24.33 $\hat{p} = \dfrac{475}{625} = 0.76$. The interval is $0.76 \pm 1.645 \sqrt{\dfrac{0.76(1-0.76)}{625}} = 0.732$ to 0.788.

24.35 $H_0 : p_{2002} = p_{2012}$ versus $H_a : p_{2002} > p_{2012}$. $\hat{p}_{2002} = \dfrac{754}{2045} = 0.3687$ and

$\hat{p}_{2012} = \dfrac{842}{2690} = 0.3130$, $\hat{p} = \dfrac{754 + 842}{2045 + 2690} = 0.3371$.

$z = \dfrac{0.3687 - 0.3130}{\sqrt{0.3371(1-0.3371)\left(\dfrac{1}{2045} + \dfrac{1}{2690}\right)}} = 4.02$ and $P = P(Z > 4.02)$, which is close to 0.

There is extremely strong evidence that the proportion of smokers in Alaska has decreased. How much of the decrease can be attributed to the campaign is uncertain.

24.37 (a) Using technology, $t = 0.392$, df $= 3.24$.

24.39 In all three cases, the observations must be able to be seen as random and representative samples of both types of diets. Also, the populations must be Normally distributed. Because the sample sizes are very small, this is almost impossible to check with typical graphical methods.

24.41 A large-sample (or plus four) confidence interval would be used for estimating a population proportion.

24.43 This is the entire population of Chicago Cubs players. Statistical inference is not appropriate.

24.45 (a) two-sample test or confidence interval for difference in proportions **(b)** two-sample test or confidence interval for difference in means **(c)** two-sample test or confidence interval for difference in proportions

24.47 (a) This is a matched pairs situation; the responses of each subject before and after treatment are not independent. **(b)** We need to know the standard deviation of the differences, not the two, individual, sample standard deviations. (Note that the mean difference is equal to the difference in the means, which is why we only need to know the standard deviation of the differences.)

24.49 (a) $\hat{p} = 80/80 = 1$, and the margin of error for 95% confidence (or any level of confidence) is 0 because $z^* \sqrt{\dfrac{(1)(1-1)}{n}} = 0$. Almost certainly, if more trials were performed, a rat would eventually make a mistake, so the actual success rate is less than 1. **(b)** The plus four estimate is $\tilde{p} = 82/84 = 0.9762$, and the plus four 95% confidence interval is $\tilde{p} \pm z^* \sqrt{\dfrac{\tilde{p}(1-\tilde{p})}{n+4}} = 0.9762 \pm 0.0326 = 0.9436$ to 1.0088. Ignoring the upper limit, we are 95% confident that the actual success rate is 0.9436 or greater.

24.51 PLAN: We test $H_0 : \mu = 12$ versus $H_a : \mu > 12$, where μ denotes the mean age at first word, measured in months. **SOLVE:** We regard the sample as an SRS; a stemplot (not shown) shows that the data are right-skewed with a high outlier (26 months). If we proceed with the t procedures despite this, we find $\bar{x} = 13$ and $s = 4.9311$ months. $t = \dfrac{13 - 12}{4.9311/\sqrt{20}} = 0.907$, with df = 19, and $P = 0.1879$. (*Note:* If you delete the outlier mentioned above, $\bar{x} = 12.3158$, $s = 3.9729$, and $t = 0.346$, yielding $P = 0.3665$; the conclusion will not change.) **CONCLUDE:** We cannot conclude that the mean age at first word is greater than one year.

24.53 PLAN: We give a 90% confidence interval for μ, the mean age at first word, measured in months. **SOLVE:** See results from Exercise 24.51. For df = 19, $t^* = 1.729$, so the 90% confidence interval is $13 \pm 1.729 \dfrac{4.9311}{\sqrt{20}} = 11.09$ to 14.91 months.

CONCLUDE: We are 90% confident that the mean age at first word for normal children is between 11 and 15 months.

24.55 (a) The design is shown below. **(b) PLAN:** We test $H_0 : \mu_B = \mu_C$ versus $H_a : \mu_B \neq \mu_C$. **SOLVE:** We have $\bar{x}_B = 41.2825$ and $s_B = 0.2550$, and $\bar{x}_C = 42.4925$ and $s_C = 0.2939$; $n_B = n_C = 8$. SE = 0.1376, and $t = \dfrac{\bar{x}_B - \bar{x}_C}{\text{SE}} = -8.79$. With df = 7 (or 13.73 from software), $P < 0.001$. Using software, with df = 13.73, $P = 0.0000$ to four places. There is overwhelming evidence that method B gives darker color on average. However, the magnitude of this difference may be too small to be important in practice.

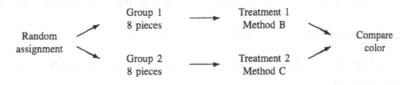

24.57 PLAN: We give a 95% confidence interval for p, the proportion of female students with at least one parent who allows drinking. SOLVE: We are told that the sample represents an SRS. Large sample methods may be used because the number of successes and the number of failures are both greater than 15. With $\hat{p} = 65/94 = 0.6915$, we have SE = 0.04764, so the margin of error is 1.96SE = 0.09337, and the interval is 0.5981 to 0.7849. CONCLUDE: With 95% confidence, the proportion of female students who have at least one parent who allows drinking is 0.598 to 0.785.

24.59 (a) PLAN: We want to compare the proportions p_1 (microwaved crackers that show checking) and p_2 (control crackers that show checking). We can do this either by testing hypotheses or with a confidence interval, but because the "microwave checked" count is only 3, significance tests are not appropriate. We will use the plus four procedure and construct a confidence interval for $p_1 - p_2$. SOLVE: We find that $\tilde{p}_1 = \dfrac{3+1}{65+2} = 0.0597$ and $\tilde{p}_2 = \dfrac{57+1}{65+2} = 0.8657$. SE = $\sqrt{\dfrac{\tilde{p}_1(1-\tilde{p}_1)}{67} + \dfrac{\tilde{p}_2(1-\tilde{p}_2)}{67}} = 0.05073$, and a 95% confidence interval is given by $\tilde{p}_1 - \tilde{p}_2 \pm 1.96(0.0507) = -0.9054$ to -0.7066. CONCLUDE: We are 95% confident that microwaving reduces the percentage of checked crackers by between 70.7% and 90.5%. **(b)** PLAN: We want to compare μ_1 and μ_2, the mean breaking pressures of microwaved and control crackers. We test $H_0 : \mu_1 = \mu_2$ versus $H_a : \mu_1 \neq \mu_2$ and construct a 95% confidence interval for $\mu_1 - \mu_2$. SOLVE: We assume the data can be considered SRS's from the two populations, and that the population distributions are not far from Normal. Now, SE = 9.0546 and $t = 6.914$, so the P-value is very small, regardless of whether we use df = 19 or df = 33.27. A 95% confidence interval for the difference in mean breaking pressures between these cracker types is 43.65 to 81.55 psi (using df = 19 and $t^* = 2.093$), or 44.18 to 81.02 psi (using df = 33.27 and $t^* = 2.0339$). CONCLUDE: There is very strong evidence that microwaving crackers changes their mean breaking strength. We are 95% confident that microwaving crackers increases their mean breaking strength by between 43.65 and 81.55 psi.

24.61 Two of the counts are too small to perform a significance test safely.

24.63 The group means are $\bar{x}_1 = 5.9$ (insulin), $\bar{x}_2 = 0.75$ (glucose) ng/ml, and the standard deviations are $s_1 = 0.9\sqrt{10} = 2.85$ and $s_2 = 0.2\sqrt{10} = 0.632$ ng/ml. PLAN: We test $H_0 : \mu_1 = \mu_2$ versus $H_a : \mu_1 \neq \mu_2$. SOLVE: The estimated standard error of the difference in sample means is SE = $\sqrt{0.9^2 + 0.2^2} = 0.9220$, so $t = \dfrac{5.9 - 0.75}{\text{SE}} = 5.59$. With either df = 9 or df = 9.89, $P < 0.001$. CONCLUDE: The evidence is even stronger than the paper claimed.

24.65 The sample proportion is $\hat{p} = 594/1484 = 0.400$. The 95% confidence interval for those who believe humans developed from earlier species of animals is

$$0.40 \pm 1.96 \sqrt{\frac{0.40(0.60)}{1484}}, \; 0.375 \text{ to } 0.425.$$

Chapter 25 – Two Categorical Variables: The Chi-Square Test

25.1 (a) The table provided gives percentages in each category. As an example, there were a total of 1308 surveyed Caucasians. Of these, 181 were under 25; the proportion of Caucasians surveyed who were under 25 is 181/1308 = 0.1384, which is represented as 13.8% in the table. **(b)** The bar graph clearly reveals that Hispanic visitors tend to be younger; over 40% of Caucasian visitors are older than 45.

	Caucasian	Hispanic
Under 25	13.8%	24.9%
25 to 34	24.8%	37.9%
35 to 44	17.7%	23.3%
45 and over	43.7%	13.9%

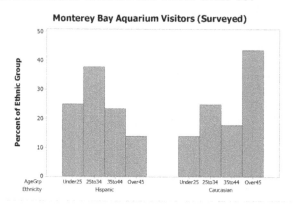

25.3 (a) To test $H_0 : p_1 = p_2$ versus $H_a : p_1 \neq p_2$ for the proportions of boys who did and did not play video games, we have $\hat{p}_1 = 0.326$ and $\hat{p}_2 = 0.336$. The pooled proportion is $\hat{p} = \dfrac{450 + 144}{1379 + 429} = 0.3285$, and SE = 0.02596, so $z = 0.39$, for which $P = 0.6966$. We conclude that we have no evidence to say the proportion of C students is different for boys who have (and have not) played video games. **(b)** To test $H_0 : p_1 = p_2$ versus $H_a : p_1 \neq p_2$ for the proportions who earn D's and F's, we have $\hat{p}_1 = 0.1400$ and $\hat{p}_2 = 0.1865$. The pooled proportion is $\hat{p} = 0.1510$, and SE = 0.01979, so $z = -2.35$, for which $P = 0.0188$. There is strong evidence that playing video games changes the proportion of boys who would earn D or F grade averages. **(c)** If we did three individual tests, we would not know how confident we could be in all three results when taken together.

25.5 (a) Expected counts are below observed counts in the table provided. For example, for Hispanics under 25, the expected count is $\dfrac{(260)(317)}{1625} = 50.72$. **(b)** We find that the observed counts are much greater than the expected counts for all three younger age groups of Hispanics. The actual count of Hispanics over 45 (44) is much smaller than the expected count (120).

	Caucasian	Hispanic	All
Under25	181	79	260
	209.3	50.7	
25to34	324	120	444
	357.4	86.6	
35to44	232	74	306
	246.3	59.7	
Over45	571	44	615
	495.0	120.0	
All	1308	317	1625

25.7 (a) All expected counts are well above 5 (the smallest is 50.72). **(b)** We test H_0 : there is no relationship between age and ethnic group for Monterey Bay Aquarium visitors versus H_a: there is a relationship between age and ethnic group. From the SAS output, we have χ^2 = 99.6058 and $P < 0.0001$. **(c)** The largest contributions generally come from the Hispanics, reflecting that that group tends to visit the aquarium at younger ages.

25.9 PLAN: We will perform a chi-square test for association between education level and opinion about astrology. We test H_0: there is no relationship between education level and astrology opinion versus H_a: there is some relationship between education level and astrology opinion. SOLVE: Examining the output provided in Figure 25.5, we see that all expected cell counts are greater than 5 (the smallest is 25.21), so conditions for use of the chi-square test are satisfied. We see that χ^2 = 3.618 and P = 0.16. CONCLUDE: There no evidence of an association between education level and opinion of astrology. Examining the table, we note that for people with graduate degrees, more than expected felt that astrology is not scientific, whereas fewer than expected believed that astrology is scientific. For people with a junior college degree, more than expected believed that astrology is scientific, and fewer than expected felt that astrology is not scientific; these differences were not large enough to believe that the differences were due to something other than sampling variability.

25.11 (a) Because there was one sample that was later categorized by two variables, this is a test of independence. **(b)** PLAN: We will test H_0: there is no relationship between age and how politically informed the person is versus H_a : there is a relationship between age and how politically informed the person is. SOLVE: Minitab output is provided. Examining the output, we see that all expected cell counts are greater than 5 (the smallest is 5.73), so conditions for use of the chi-square test are satisfied. We see that χ^2 = 32.057 on df = 12, and P = 0.001 to three decimal places. CONCLUDE: Age and being informed about politics are related. In particular, we can see that people 20 to 29 years old are less likely to be informed (observed counts are larger than expected for the cells with little awareness and smaller than expected for cells with much awareness). The other large contribution to the chi-square statistic came from people 40 to 49 years old: fewer than expected said they were not at all informed.

	Not at all	A little	Somewhat	Very	Extremely	All
20 - 29	8	29	28	13	0	78
	10.26	37.18	35.90	16.67	0.00	100.00
	5.73	17.57	31.40	17.57	5.73	78.00
	0.8977	7.4379	0.3680	1.1881	5.7316	*
30 - 39	15	28	55	23	9	130
	11.54	21.54	42.31	17.69	6.92	100.00
	9.55	29.28	52.33	29.28	9.55	130.00
	3.1062	0.0561	0.1360	1.3474	0.0320	*
40 - 49	2	25	49	26	14	116
	1.72	21.55	42.24	22.41	12.07	100.00
	8.52	26.13	46.70	26.13	8.52	116.00
	4.9932	0.0487	0.1136	0.0006	3.5180	*
50 and older	21	59	120	79	23	302
	6.95	19.54	39.74	26.16	7.62	100.00
	22.19	68.02	121.57	68.02	22.19	302.00
	0.0640	1.1967	0.0203	1.7716	0.0294	*
All	46	141	252	141	46	626
	7.35	22.52	40.26	22.52	7.35	100.00
	46.00	141.00	252.00	141.00	46.00	626.00
	*	*	*	*	*	*

Cell Contents: Count
                   % of Row
                   Expected count
                   Contribution to Chi-square

Pearson Chi-Square = 32.057, DF = 12, P-Value = 0.001

25.13 (a) df $= (r-1)(c-1) = (2-1)(3-1) = 2$ **(b)** The computed value (6.739) is between the table values 5.99 and 7.38; we conclude that $0.025 < P < 0.05$, which is consistent with output's reported $P = 0.034$. **(c)** Under the null hypothesis of no association, the mean value of χ^2 is df $= 2$. Our computed value is larger than this. The small P-value suggests that random chance does not easily explain the larger than expected value of χ^2.

25.15 (a) If all days were equally likely, we would have $p_1 = p_2 = \ldots = p_7 = \dfrac{1}{7}$, and we would expect 100 births on each day. **(b)** The chi-square statistic is then

$$\chi^2 = \frac{(84-100)^2}{100} + \frac{(110-100)^2}{100} + \cdots + \frac{(72-100)^2}{100} = 19.12.$$ **(c)** The degrees of freedom

are df $= 7 - 1 = 6$. From Table D, $\chi^2 = 19.12$ yields $0.0025 < P < 0.005$. Software gives $P = 0.004$. We have strong evidence that births are not spread evenly across the week.

25.17 (a) 15/33 = 0.455, or 45.5% of subjects chose position 1. Similarly, the percentages for each position are 15.2% for position 2, 6.1% for position 3, and 33.3% for position 4. **(b)** If subjects are equally likely to select any position, then we would expect 33/4 = 8.25 subjects in each position. **(c)** STATE: Are positions equally likely to be selected by subjects? PLAN: We test $H_0 : p_1 = p_2 = p_3 = p_4 = \frac{1}{4}$ versus H_a: the four order selection probabilities are not equally likely. SOLVE: As computed above, we expect 8.25 subjects per cell under the null hypothesis, so all expected cell counts exceed 5. Also, we have at least one observation per cell. Conditions for the chi-square test are satisfied. Now,

$$\chi^2 = \frac{(15-8.25)^2}{8.25} + \frac{(5-8.25)^2}{8.25} + \frac{(2-8.25)^2}{8.25} + \frac{(11-8.25)^2}{8.25} = 12.45.$$ The degrees of freedom are df = 4 − 1 = 3. From Table D, χ^2 = 12.45 yields 0.005 < P < 0.01 (P = 0.006 from technology). CONCLUDE: There is strong evidence that positions are not selected with equal probability—some positions are more likely to be selected than others. **(d)** We see that the largest contributions to χ^2 are from the first and third positions. In the first and fourth cases, we have more observations than expected, and in the second and third positions we have fewer observations than expected. There is evidence of *both* primacy and recency effects.

25.19 (a) 295 + 655 + 239 + 363 = 1552

25.21 (a) For those 23 to 30 years old, the percentage is 26.5%.

25.23 (a) The expected cell count is (1571)(1552)/4111 = 593.09.

25.25 (a) df = $(r-1)(c-1) = (4-1)(2-1) = 3$

25.27 (b) This is the hypothesis of association between "age" and "type of injury."

25.29 (b) We assume that the sample is an SRS, or essentially an SRS, from all weightlifting injuries.

25.31 (a) These were separate random samples, so this is a test of homogeneity. **(b)** STATE: We want to determine if the distribution of age for those with a landline differs from the distribution of those with only a cell phone. PLAN: We test H_0: the distribution of age groups is the same for landline and cell-only individuals versus H_a: the distributions are different. SOLVE: All expected cell counts are more than 5, so the guidelines for the chi-square test are satisfied. We have χ^2 = 1032.892, df = 3, and P < 0.0005. CONCLUDE: There is strong evidence of an association between age group and the type of telephone. In fact, the younger age groups were much more likely than expected to have only cell phones.

	Cell Only	Landline	All
Age18-29	374	335	709

```
                      52.75     47.25   100.00
                      115         594      709
                      587.04    113.20      *

Age30-49               347        1242     1589
                      21.84      78.16   100.00
                      257         1332     1589
                      31.63       6.10       *

Age50-64               146        1625     1771
                       8.24      91.76   100.00
                      286         1485     1771
                      68.75      13.26       *

Age65up                 36        1481     1517
                       2.37      97.63   100.00
                      245         1272     1517
                     178.51      34.42       *

All                    903        4683     5586
                      16.17      83.83   100.00
                      903         4683     5586
                         *          *        *
```

```
Cell Contents:        Count
                      % of Row
                      Expected count
                      Contribution to Chi-square
```

```
Pearson Chi-Square = 1032.892, DF = 3, P-Value = 0.000
```

25.33 (a) The diagram is shown below. To perform the randomization, label the infants 01 to 77, and choose pairs of random digits. **(b)** See the Minitab output for the two-way table. We find $\chi^2 = 0.568$, df = 3, and $P = 0.904$. There is no reason to doubt that the randomization "worked."

```
              Female      Male

NLCP              11         8
               10.36      8.64
              0.03907    0.04689

PBM               11         9
               10.91      9.09
              0.00076    0.00091

PL-LCP            11         8
               10.36      8.64
              0.03907    0.04689

TG-LCP             9        10
               10.36      8.64
              0.17943    0.21531
```

```
Cell Contents:        Count
                      Expected count
                      Contribution to Chi-square
```

```
Pearson Chi-Square = 0.568, DF = 3, P-Value = 0.904
Likelihood Ratio Chi-Square = 0.567, DF = 3, P-Value = 0.904
```

25.35 (a) The two-way table follows. We test $H_0 : p_1 = p_2$ versus $H_a : p_1 < p_2$. **(b)** The z test must be used because the chi-square procedure measures evidence in support of any association and is implicitly two-sided. We have $\hat{p}_1 = 0.3667$ and $\hat{p}_2 = 0.7333$. The pooled proportion is $\hat{p} = (11+22)/(30+30) = 0.55$, and the standard error is SE = 0.12845, so z = –2.85, and P = 0.0022. We have strong evidence that rats that can stop the shock (and, therefore, presumably have better attitudes) develop tumors less often than rats that cannot (and, therefore, are presumably depressed).

	Tumor	No Tumor
Group 1	11	19
Group 2	22	8

25.37 STATE: Does sexual content of ads differ in magazines aimed at different audiences? PLAN: We test H_0: there is no relationship between sexual content of ads and magazine audience versus H_a: there is some relationship between sexual content of ads and magazine audience. SOLVE: Examining the Minitab output in Figure 25.9, we see that conditions for use of the chi-square test are satisfied because all expected cell counts exceed 5 (the smallest is 82.4). We have $\chi^2 = 80.874$ with df = 2, leading to P < 0.0005. CONCLUDE: Magazines aimed at women are much more likely to have sexual depictions of models than the other two types of magazines. Specifically, about 39% of ads in women's magazines show sexual depictions of models, compared with 21% and 17% of ads in general-audience and men's magazines, respectively. The two women's chi-squared terms account for over half of the total chi-square value.

25.39 We need cell counts, not just percentages. If we had been given the number of travelers in each group—leisure and business—we could have estimated this.

25.41 In order to do a chi-square test, each subject can only be counted once. In this experiment, each individual is represented for both treatments (carob and chocolate).

25.43 (a) We test H_0: there is no relationship between degree held and service attendance versus H_a: there is some relationship between degree held and service attendance. Examining the Minitab output, $\chi^2 = 14.19$ with df = 3, and P-value = 0.003. There is strong evidence of an association between degree held and service attendance.

```
            HS    JColl   Bachelor   Graduate    All

No         880     101       232        105     1318
         842.7   107.3     248.9      119.2   1318.0

Yes        400      62       146         76      684
         437.3    55.7     129.1       61.8    684.0

Cell Contents:         Count
                       Expected count

Pearson Chi-Square = 14.190, DF = 3, P-Value = 0.003
```

(b) The new table is shown below. We find $\chi^2 = 0.73$ on df = 2, and $P = 0.694$. In this table, we find no evidence of association between religious service attendance and degree held.

```
           JColl   Bachelor   Graduate    All

No          101       232        105      438
           98.9     229.3      109.8    438.0

Yes          62       146         76      284
           64.1     148.7       71.2    284.0

Cell Contents:         Count
                       Expected count

Pearson Chi-Square = 0.729, DF = 2, P-Value = 0.694
```

(c) The new table is shown. We have $\chi^2 = 13.40$ with df = 1. $P = 0.000$ to three decimal places (it's actually 0.0002). There is overwhelming evidence of association between level of education (High School versus Beyond High School) and religious service attendance.

```
          BeyondHS  HSchool     All

Attend        284      400      684
            246.7    437.3    684.0

NoAttend      438      880     1318
            475.3    842.7   1318.0

Cell Contents:         Count
                       Expected count

Pearson Chi-Square = 13.416, DF = 1, P-Value = 0.000
```

(d) In general, we find that people with degrees beyond high school attend services more often than expected; people with high school degrees attend services less often than expected. Of those with high school degrees, 31.3% attended services, and the percentages are 38.0%, 38.6%, and 42.0%, respectively, for people with junior college, bachelor's, and graduate degrees.

25.45 STATE: Is there a relationship between race and parental opinion of schools? PLAN: We use a chi-square test to test H_0: there is no relationship between race and opinion about schools versus H_a: there is some relationship between race and opinion about schools. SOLVE: All expected cell counts exceed 5 (the smallest is 21.26), so use of a chi-square test is appropriate. We find that χ^2 = 22.426 with df = 8, and P = 0.004. Nearly half of the total chi-square comes from the first two terms; most of the rest comes from the second and fifth rows. CONCLUDE: We have strong evidence of a relationship between race and opinion of schools. Specifically, according to the sample (as illustrated in the table), blacks are less likely and Hispanics are more likely to consider schools to be excellent, while Hispanics and whites differ in the percent considering schools good. Also, a higher percentage of blacks rated schools as "fair."

```
               Black    Other    White      All

Exclnt            12       22       34       68
               22.70    22.59    22.70    68.00

Good              69       81       55      205
               68.45    68.11    68.45   205.00

Fair              75       60       61      196
               65.44    65.12    65.44   196.00

Poor              24       24       24       72
               24.04    23.92    24.04    72.00

Don'tKnow         22       14       28       64
               21.37    21.26    21.37    64.00

Cell Contents:          Count
                        Expected count

Pearson Chi-Square = 22.426, DF = 8, P-Value = 0.004
```

25.47 PLAN: We compare how the number of children per group has changed from 2009 through 2013 at the Monterey Bay Aquarium. We will create a bar graph and do a chi-square test of homogeneity (each year is a separate sample). SOLVE: To examine any possible change in the number of children per group, we first look at a segmented bar graph

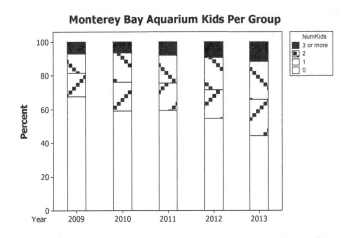

of the data. The graph indicates that the number of groups with no children has been steadily decreasing, and the number of groups with three or more children has been increasing slightly. There is some fluctuation in the number of groups with one or two children, but 2013 definitely has more of these groups than 2009.

First, we note that all expected counts are above 5 (the smallest is 49.3). The test statistic is $\chi^2 = 75.248$ with df = 12. With *P*-value < 0.0005, we reject the null hypothesis that there has been no change in the distribution of the number of children per group. It seems clear (especially when comparing 2009 to 2013) that they are meeting their goal of attracting a younger audience.

```
Rows: NumKids   Columns: Year

            2009    2010    2011    2012    2013     All

0            390     330     342     318     268    1648
           327.6   316.7   327.6   331.5   344.6  1648.0

1             79      94      93      99     131     496
            98.6    95.3    98.6    99.8   103.7   496.0

2             66      96      96     111     137     506
           100.6    97.3   100.6   101.8   105.8   506.0

3 or more     41      37      45      55      70     248
            49.3    47.7    49.3    49.9    51.9   248.0

All          576     557     576     583     606    2898
           576.0   557.0   576.0   583.0   606.0  2898.0

Cell Contents:       Count
                     Expected count

Pearson Chi-Square = 75.248, DF = 12, P-Value = 0.000
```

25.49 STATE: How do the conditional distributions of political leaning, given education, compare? PLAN: We compare the percentages leaning toward each party within each education group. SOLVE: The requested table is provided. At each education level, we compute the percentage leaning toward each party. For example, among bachelor's degree holders, 166/(166 + 136) = 54.97% lean Democrat, whereas the other 45.03% lean Republican.

```
        Bachelor  Graduate  Highschool  JrCollege    None     All

Dem          166       119         454         68     127     934
           54.97     69.19       59.66      57.14   70.95   60.93

Rep          136        53         307         51      52     599
           45.03     30.81       40.34      42.86   29.05   39.07

Cell Contents:       Count
                     % of Column
```

CONCLUDE: At every education level, people leaning Democrat outweigh people leaning Republican. The difference is greatest at the "None" level of education, then it decreases until the party support is nearly equal for bachelor's degree holders. Among graduate degree holders, Democrats strongly outnumber Republicans.

25.51 is a Web-based exercise.

Chapter 26 – Inference for Regression

26.1 (a) A scatterplot of the data is provided, along with the least-squares regression line (students were not asked to add the line). We see that there is a strong, positive, linear relationship between wine intake and relative risk. From software, the correlation is $r = \sqrt{0.970} = 0.985$. **(b)** If we knew it, the slope β would tell us how much the relative risk of breast cancer changes in women for each increase of 1 gram of wine per day (on average). The

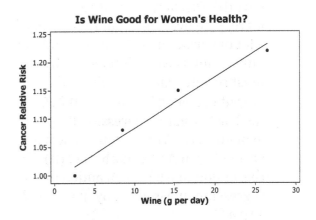

estimate of β is $b = 0.009012$ (see output). We estimate that an increase in intake of 1 gram per day increases relative risk of breast cancer by about 0.009. The estimate of α is $a = 0.9931$. According to our estimate, wine intake of 0 grams per day is associated with a relative risk of breast cancer of 0.9931 (about 1).

Regression Analysis: Risk versus Wine

```
The regression equation is Risk = 0.993 + 0.00901 Wine

Predictor     Coef   SE Coef      T      P
Constant   0.99309   0.01777  55.88  0.000
Wine      0.009012  0.001112   8.10  0.015

S = 0.0198583   R-Sq = 97.0%   R-Sq(adj) = 95.6%
```

(c) The least-squares regression line is given by $\hat{y} = 0.9931 + 0.0090x$. The table below summarizes computed residuals, which sum to zero, as demonstrated. We also have $s^2 = 0.00079/2 = 0.000395$, which provides an estimate of σ^2. We estimate σ by $s = \sqrt{\dfrac{0.00079}{4-2}} = 0.01987$, which agrees (up to rounding error) with "S" in the output above.

x	y	$\hat{y}$	Residual $(y-\hat{y})$	$(y-\hat{y})^2$
2.5	1.00	1.0156	−0.0156	0.00024
8.5	1.08	1.0697	0.0103	0.00011
15.5	1.15	1.1328	0.0172	0.00030
26.5	1.22	1.2319	−0.0119	0.00014
			0	0.00079

26.3 (a) A scatterplot of discharge by year is provided, along with the fitted regression line, which is requested in part (b). Discharge seems to be increasing over time, but there is also a lot of variation in this trend, and our impression is easily influenced by the most recent years' data. From the output provided below, $r^2 = 0.215$, so the least-squares regression line explains 21.5% of the total observed variability in Arctic discharge. **(b)** The

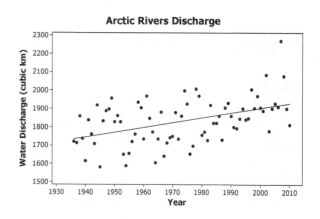

regression line has been added to the scatterplot provided. The least-squares regression line is given by $\hat{y} = -3362 + 2.6327x$. We see from the output that $s = 110.477$.

```
The regression equation is Water = - 3362 + 2.63 Year

Predictor     Coef   SE Coef        T       P
Constant     -3362      1163    -2.89   0.005
Year        2.6327    0.5893     4.47   0.000

S = 110.477   R-Sq = 21.5%   R-Sq(adj) = 20.4%
```

26.5 Refer to the output provided with the solution to Exercise 26.3. We test $H_0 : \beta = 0$ versus $H_a : \beta > 0$. We compute $t = \dfrac{b}{SE_b} = \dfrac{2.6327}{0.5893} = 4.47$. Here, df $= n - 2 = 75$ $- 2 = 73$. In referring to Table C, we round df down to df $= 60$. Using Table C, we obtain $P < 0.0005$. Using software, we obtain $P = 0.000$ (rounded to three decimal places). There is strong evidence of an increase in Arctic discharge over time.

26.7 (a) Refer to the solution of Exercise 26.4. For testing $H_0 : \beta = 0$ versus $H_a : \beta > 0$, we have $t = 8.104$ with df $= 2$. For the one-sided alternative suggested, we obtained $0.005 < P < 0.01$. This test is equivalent to testing H_0 : population correlation $= 0$ versus H_a : population correlation > 0. **(b)** Using software, $r = 0.985$. This can also be computed by referring to the Minitab output provided with Exercise 26.1, with $r = +\sqrt{r^2} = +\sqrt{0.97}$. Referring to Table E with $n = 4$, we find that $0.005 < P < 0.01$, just as in part (a). These tests are equivalent.

26.9 Referring to Table C, $t^* = 2.920$ (df $= 4 - 2 = 2$, with 90% confidence). A 90% confidence interval for β is given by $0.009012 \pm 2.920(0.001112) = 0.009012 \pm 0.003247 = 0.00577$ to 0.01226. With 90% confidence, the expected increase in relative risk of breast cancer associated with an increase in alcohol consumption by 1 gram per day is between 0.00577 and 0.01226.

26.11 Refer to the output provided in the solution to Exercise 26.3. We have $b = 2.6327$ and $SE_b = 0.5893$. With 75 observations, df = 73. Using Table C, we look under the row corresponding to df = 60 (the nearest smaller value of df in the table). We obtain $t^* = 1.671$ ($t^* = 1.666$ from software). A 90% confidence interval for β is given by $2.6327 \pm 1.671(0.5893) = 2.6327 \pm 0.9847 = 1.6480$ to 3.6174 cubic kilometers per year (software: 1.6509 to 3.6145). With 90% confidence, the yearly increase in Arctic discharge is between 1.6480 and 3.6174 cubic kilometers. This confidence interval excludes "0," so there is evidence that Arctic discharge is increasing over time.

26.13 (a) If $x^* = 0.65$, then our prediction for mean volume is $\hat{\mu} = 10.0655 + 86.0308\,(0.65) = 65.98552$. **(b)** We have $SE_{\hat{\mu}} = 1.47$. For df = 29 − 2 = 27 and 95% confidence, we have $t^* = 2.052$. A 95% confidence interval for mean brain gray-matter volume in people with 0.65 AROC is given by $65.98552 \pm 2.052(1.469) = 62.971$ to 69.000.

```
    Fit    SE Fit        95% CI               95% PI
65.9855  1.46902  (62.9714, 68.9997)  (49.4805, 82.4906)
```

26.15 (a) The residual plot provided does not suggest any deviation from a straight-line relationship between brain volume and Aroc score, although there are two large (in absolute value) residuals near the left end of the plot. Both babies had Aroc scores of about 0.63, but one child had his/her IQ underpredicted (the positive residual) and one child was overpredicted (the negative residual). **(b)** A stemplot of residuals, provided below, does not suggest that the distribution of residuals departs strongly from Normality. The value 22 from observation 5 may be an outlier; other than that, the residuals are symmetric and mound-shaped. **(c)** It is reasonable to assume that observations are independent because we have 29 different subjects, who are measured separately. **(d)** Other than the large residuals noted in part (a), there is no indication that variability changes; there are fewer babies with low Aroc scores, so there is naturally less variability on the left end of the plot.

Stem and Leaf

Stem	Leaf	Count
2	2	1
1		
1	2	1
0	889	3
0	222333334	9
-0	44432110	8
-0	88777	5
-1	0	1
-1	8	1
-2		

-1|8 represents -18

26.17 (a) With a positive association, $r = +\sqrt{r^2} = +\sqrt{0.579} = 0.761$.

26.19 (a) This is a one-sided alternative because we wonder if larger appraisal values are associated with larger selling prices.

26.21 (c) $s = 221.341$

26.23 (b) With 45 degrees of freedom, $t^* = 2.014$, so the margin of error is $2.014(0.1540) = 0.3102$. Using Table C and 40 df, $t^* = 2.021$ and ME $= 0.3112$.

26.25 (a) Scientists estimate that each additional 1% increase in the percentage of Bt cotton plants results in an average increase of 6.81 mirid bugs per 100 plants. **(b)** The regression model explains 90% of the variability in mirid bug density. That is, knowledge of the proportion of Bt cotton plants explains almost all of the variation in mirid bug density. **(c)** Recall that the test $H_0 : \beta = 0$ versus $H_a : \beta > 0$ is exactly the same as the test H_0 : population correlation = 0 versus H_a : population correlation > 0. Because $P < 0.0001$, there is strong evidence of a positive linear relationship between the proportion of Bt cotton plants and the density of mirid bugs. **(d)** We may conclude that denser mirid bug populations are associated with larger proportions of Bt cotton plants. However, it seems plausible that a reduced use of pesticides (an indirect cause) instead of more Bt cotton plants (a direct cause) is the reason for this increase.

26.27 For 90% intervals with df = 10, use $t^* = 1.812$. **(a)** Use the estimated slope and standard error given in Figure 26.13. The confidence interval for β is $b \pm t^* SE_b = 274.78 \pm 1.812(88.18) = 274.78 \pm 159.78 = 115.0$ to 434.6 fps/inch. **(b)** This is the "90% CI" given in Figure 26.13: 176.2 to 239.4 fps. To confirm this, we can use the given values of $\hat{y} = 207.8$ and $SE_\mu = 17.4$, labeled "Fit" and "SE Fit" in the output: $\hat{y} \pm t^* SE_\mu = 207.8 \pm 1.812(17.4) = 176.3$ to 239.3 fps, which agrees with the output up to rounding error.

26.29 (a) The stemplot has split stems. There is little evidence of non-Normality in the residuals, and there don't appear to be any outliers. **(b)** The scatterplot confirms the comments made in the text: There is no clear pattern, but the variability about the "residual = 0" line may be slightly greater when x is larger. **(c)** Presumably, close inspection of a manatee's corpse will reveal nonsubtle clues when the cause of death is from collision with a boat propeller. It seems

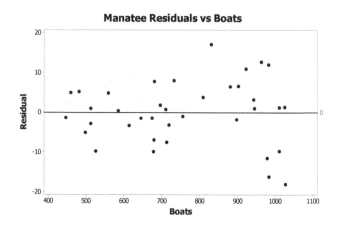

reasonable that the kills listed in the table are mostly not caused by pollution.

```
-1 | 86
-1 | 2000
-0 | 775
-0 | 33321111
 0 | 011111234
 0 | 5556788
 1 | 123
 1 | 7
```

26.31 (a) This is a confidence interval for β. With df = 35, using the table (and rounding degrees of freedom down to 30), we have $t^* = 2.042$, so a 95% confidence interval for β is $b \pm t^* \mathrm{SE}_b = 0.132259 \pm 2.042(0.007067) = 0.132259 \pm 0.014431 = 0.11783$ to 0.14669 additional killed manatees per 1000 additional boats. (Using technology, df = 34, and $t^* = 2.030$, we have 0.11791 to 0.14661 additional killed manatees per 1000 additional boats.) **(b)** With 900,000 boats, we predict $\hat{y} = -44.831 + 0.132259(900) = 74.2021$ killed manatees, which agrees with the output in Figure 26.14 under "Fit." We need the prediction interval because we are forecasting the number of manatees killed for a single year. According to the output provided, a 95% prediction interval for the number of killed manatees is 57.74 to 90.67 kills if 900,000 boats are registered.

26.33 See the JMP output below. **(a)** We test H_0 : population correlation = 0 against H_a : population correlation > 0; recall this is equivalent to a test for $\beta > 0$. We see that $t = 4.06$ with df = 30 − 2 = 28. So, $P = 0.0004$. There is very strong evidence of a positive correlation between Gray's forecasted number of storms and the number of storms that actually occur. **(b)** The output provides the confidence interval for the mean number of storms in years for which Gray predicts 16 storms (use the line for 2011). Here, $\hat{\mu} = 1.6681676 + 0.9199861(16) = 16.388$, and JMP gives the 95% confidence interval for the mean as 14.077 to 18.699.

Parameter Estimates

Term	Estimate	Std Error	t Ratio	Prob>|t|
Intercept	1.6681676	2.828416	0.59	0.5601
Forecast	0.9199861	0.22643	4.06	0.0004*

Year	Forecast	Observed	Lower 95% Mean...	Upper 95% Mean...
2001	12	15	11.268410395	14.147592376
2002	11	12	10.261391967	13.314638515
2003	14	16	12.860700306	16.235247044
2004	14	14	12.860700306	16.235247044
2005	15	27	13.49831086	17.43760878
2006	17	10	14.618034297	19.997829921
2007	17	14	14.618034297	19.997829921
2008	15	16	13.49831086	17.43760878
2009	11	9	10.261391967	13.314638515
2010	18	19	15.13616182	21.319674688
2011	16	19	14.076582017	18.699309912

26.35 The stemplot is provided, where residuals are rounded to the nearest tenth. The plot suggests that the residuals may not follow a Normal distribution. Specifically, there is a low outlier that seems extreme. This makes regression inference and interval procedures unreliable.

Stem and Leaf

Stem	Leaf	Count
1	2	1
1		
0		
0	6	1
0	5	1
0	2222333	7
0	1111	4
-0	11000	5
-0	3333322	7
-0	554	3
-0	7	1
-0		

0|7 represents -7

26.37 (a) Shown is the scatterplot with two (nearly identical) regression lines: one using all points, and one with the outlier omitted. The Minitab output for both regressions is provided. **(b)** The correlation for all points is $r = 0.8486$. For testing the slope, $t = 6.00$, for which $P < 0.0005$. **(c)** Without the outlier, $r = 0.7014$, the test statistic for the slope is $t = 3.55$, and $P = 0.004$. In both cases, there is strong evidence of a linear relationship between neural loss aversion and behavioral loss aversion. However, omitting the outlier weakens this evidence somewhat.

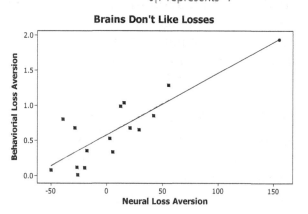

Regression output (all points)

```
The regression equation is
Behave = 0.585 + 0.00879 Neural

Predictor    Coef   SE Coef     T      P
Constant   0.58496  0.07093  8.25  0.000
Neural     0.008794 0.001465 6.00  0.000

S = 0.279729   R-Sq = 72.0%
```

Regression output (without outlier)

```
The regression equation is
Behave = 0.586 + 0.00891 Neural

Predictor    Coef   SE Coef     T      P
Constant   0.58581  0.07506  7.80  0.000
Neural     0.008909 0.002510 3.55  0.004

S = 0.290252   R-Sq = 49.2%
```

26.39 The distribution is skewed right, but the sample is large, so t procedures should be safe. We find $\bar{x} = 0.2781$ g/m^2 and $s = 0.1803$ g/m^2. Table C gives $t^* = 1.984$ for df = 100 (rounded down from 115). The 95% confidence interval for μ is $0.2871 \pm (1.981)(0.1803/\sqrt{116}) = 0.2449$ to 0.3113 g/m^2. (Using df = 115, we have $t^* = 1.981$, and the 95%

confidence interval for μ is identical.)

26.41 PLAN: We examine the relationship between pine cone abundance and squirrel density using a scatterplot and regression. SOLVE: A scatterplot indicates a positive relationship that is roughly linear with what appears to be an outlier at the upper right of the graph. Regression gives predicted squirrel density as $\hat{y} = 0.961 + 0.205x$. The slope is significantly different from zero

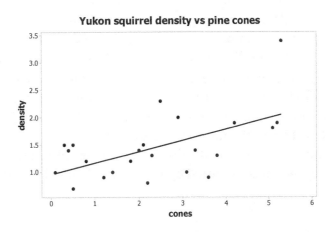

($t = 3.13$, $P = 0.005$). To assess the evidence that more cones leads to more offspring, we should use the one-sided alternative, $H_a : \beta > 0$, for which P is half as large (so $P = 0.0025$). The conditions for inference seem to be violated. The residual plot shows what appears to be increasing variability with increasing cone values, as well as the outlier already mentioned. The stemplot of the residuals indicates two large positive outliers; the distribution may be right-skewed. CONCLUDE: We seem to have strong evidence of a positive linear relationship between cone abundance and squirrel density; however, conditions for inference may not be satisfied.

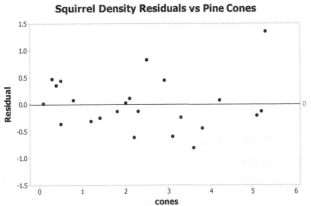

-0	76
-0	54
-0	33222
-0	111
0	00001
0	3
0	444
0	
0	8
1	
1	3

Regression Analysis: density versus cones

```
Coefficients

Term        Coef   SE Coef   T-Value   P-Value   VIF
Constant   0.961    0.188      5.12     0.000
cones     0.2053   0.0657      3.13     0.005    1.00


       S      R-sq
0.501448   31.75%
```

26.43 PLAN: We will examine the relationship between beaver stumps and beetle larvae using a scatterplot and regression. We specifically wish to test for a positive slope β and find a confidence interval for β. SOLVE: The scatterplot shows a positive linear association; the regression line is $\hat{y} = -1.286 + 11.894x$. A stemplot of the residuals does not suggest non-Normality of the residuals, the residual plot does not suggest nonlinearity, and the problem description makes clear that observations are independent. To test $H_0 : \beta = 0$ versus $H_a : \beta > 0$, the test statistic is $t = 10.47$ (df = 21), for which Table C provides a one-sided P-value, $P < 0.0005$. For df = 21, $t^* = 2.080$ for 95% confidence, so with b and SE_b as given by Minitab, we are 95% confident that β is between $11.894 \pm (2.080)(1.136) = 9.531$ and 14.257. CONCLUDE: We have strong evidence that beetle larvae counts increase with beaver stump counts. Specifically, we are 95% confident that each additional stump is (on average) accompanied by between 9.5 and 14.3 additional larvae clusters.

```
The regression equation is Larvae = - 1.29 + 11.9 Stumps
                                                          -1 | 300
Predictor     Coef   SE Coef      T      P               -0 | 965
Constant    -1.286     2.853  -0.45  0.657               -0 | 3222
Stumps      11.894     1.136  10.47  0.000                0 | 0122344
                                                          0 | 56772.08189
S = 6.41939   R-Sq = 83.9%   R-Sq(adj) = 83.1%
```

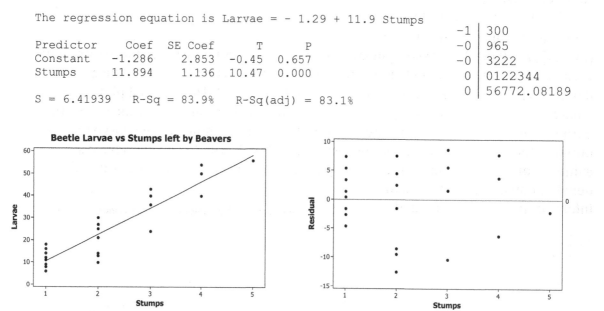

26.45 PLAN: Using a scatterplot and regression, we examine how well phytopigment concentration explains DNA concentration. SOLVE: The scatterplot shows a fairly strong, linear, positive association; the regression equation is $\hat{y} = 0.1523 + 8.1676x$. A stemplot of the residuals looks reasonably Normal, but the scatterplot suggests that the variability about the line is greater when phytopigment concentration is greater. This may make regression inference unreliable, but we will proceed. Finally, observations are independent, from the context of the problem. The slope is significantly different from 0 ($t = 13.25$, df = 114, $P < 0.001$). We might also construct a 95% confidence interval for β: $8.1676 \pm 1.984(0.6163) = 6.95$ to 9.39 (the 95% confidence interval is identical if we use df = 114). CONCLUDE: The significant linear relationship between phytopigment and DNA concentrations is consistent with the belief that organic matter settling is a primary source of DNA. Starting from a measurement of phytopigment concentration, we could give a fairly accurate prediction of DNA concentration, because the linear relationship explains about $r^2 = 60.6\%$ of the variation in DNA concentration. We are 95% confident that

each additional unit increase in phytopigment concentration increases DNA
concentration by between 6.95 and 9.39 units (on average).

```
The regression equation is DNA = 0.152 +
8.17 Phyto

Predictor      Coef   SE Coef      T      P
Constant    0.15231   0.01419  10.73  0.000
Phyto        8.1676    0.6163  13.25  0.000

S = 0.113612    R-Sq = 60.6%
```

```
-3 | 32
-2 | 5
-2 | 42
-1 | 76
-1 | 443321000
-0 | 99998888876666666655555
-0 | 44433333322222100000
 0 | 00001111111222223333444444
 0 | 66678899
 1 | 0011112233444
 1 | 678999
 2 | 13
 2 | 59
```

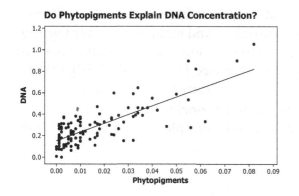

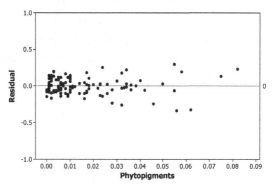

26.47 (a) The mean is $\bar{x} = -0.00333$, and the standard deviation is
$s = 1.0233$. For a standardized set of values, we expect the mean and
standard deviation to be (up to rounding error) 0 and 1, respectively.
(b) The stemplot does not look particularly symmetric, but it is not
strikingly non-Normal for such a small sample. **(c)** The probability that
a standard Normal variable is as extreme as this is about 0.0272.

```
-2 | 2
-1 |
-1 | 4
-0 |
-0 | 32
 0 | 01122
 0 | 7
 1 | 0
 1 | 5
```

26.49 For df = 14 and a 95% confidence interval, we use $t^* = 2.145$, so the interval is
$-0.01270 \pm 2.145(0.01264) = -0.0398$ to 0.0144. This interval does contain 0.

26.51 is a Web-based exercise.

Chapter 27 – One-Way Analysis of Variance: Comparing Several Means

27.1 (a) The null hypothesis is "all age groups have the same (population) mean road-rage measurement," and the alternative is "at least one group has a different mean." **(b)** The F test is quite significant, giving strong evidence that the means are different. The sample means suggest that the degree of road rage decreases with age. (We assume that higher numbers indicate *more* road rage.)

27.3 (a) The stemplots appear to suggest that logging reduces the number of trees per plot and that recovery is slow (the one-year-after and eight-years-after logging stemplots are similar). **(b)** The means lead one to the same conclusion as in part (a): The first mean (23.75) is much larger than the other two (14.08 and 15.78). **(c)** In testing $H_0 : \mu_1 = \mu_2 = \mu_3$ versus H_a : not all means are the same, we find that $F =$ 11.43 with df = 2 and 30, which has $P = 0.0002$, so we conclude that these differences are significant: The mean number of trees per plot is significantly lower in logged areas.

```
Never logged     1 year ago     8 years ago
0                0 | 2           0 | 4
0                0 | 9           0 |
1                1 | 2244        1 | 22
1 | 699          1 | 57789       1 | 5889
2 | 0124         2 | 0           2 | 22
2 | 7789         2 |             2 |
3 | 3            3 |             3 |
```

27.5 (a) Answers will vary due to randomness. **(b)** By moving the middle mean to the same level as the other two, it is possible to reduce F to about 0.02, which has a P-value very close to the left end of the scale (near 1). **(c)** By moving any mean up or down (or any two means in opposite directions), the value of F increases (and P decreases) until it moves to the right end of the scale.

27.7 (a) We have $s_1^2 = 25.6591$, $s_2^2 = 24.8106$, and $s_3^2 = 33.1944$, so $s_1 = 5.065$, $s_2 =$ 4.981 and $s_3 = 5.761$. The ratio of largest to smallest standard deviation is 5.761/4.981 = 1.16, which is less than 2. Conditions are satisfied. **(b)** The three standard deviations are $s_L = 17.41$, $s_M = 18.13$, and $s_C = 17.42$. The ratio of largest to smallest standard deviation is 18.13/17.41 = 1.04, which is less than 2. Conditions are satisfied.

27.9 STATE: How does the presence of nitrogen, phosphorus, or both affect the development of new leaves in bromeliads? PLAN: Examine the data to compare the effect of the treatments and check that we can safely use ANOVA. If the data allow ANOVA, assess the significance of observed differences in mean numbers of new leaves. SOLVE: Side-by-side stemplots shows some irregularity but no outliers or strong skewness. The Minitab ANOVA output below shows that the group standard deviations easily satisfy our rule of thumb ($2.059/1.302 = 1.58 < 2$). The differences among the groups were significant at $\alpha = 0.05$: $F = 3.44$, df = 3 and 27, $P = 0.031$. CONCLUDE: Nitrogen had a positive effect, the phosphorus and control groups were similar, and the plants that got both nutrients fell between the others.

Control	Nitrogen	Phosphorus	Both
11	00	11	11	0	11	
12	0	12	12	0	12	
13	0	13	0	13	0	13	0
14		14	0	14	000	14	0000
15	00	15	00	15	00	15	0
16	0	16	0	16		16	0
17		17	00	17		17	0
18		18	0	18		18	

Minitab output

Source	DF	SS	MS	F	P
Treatment	3	27.21	9.07	3.44	0.031
Error	27	71.18	2.64		
Total	30	98.39			

Individual 95% CIs For Mean
Based on Pooled StDev

Level	N	Mean	StDev
C	7	13.286	2.059
N	8	15.625	1.685
P	8	13.500	1.414
NP	8	14.625	1.302

Pooled StDev = 1.624

```
Individual 95% CIs For Mean
Based on Pooled StDev
-----------+---------+---------+------
(--------*-------)
                            (-------*-------)
     (--------*-------)
                (------*-------)
-----------+---------+---------+------
          13.5      15.0      16.5
```

27.11 (a) $I = 3$ and $N = 96$, so df = 2 and 93. **(b)** $I = 3$ and $N = 90$, so df = 2 and 87.

27.13 (a) No sample standard deviation is larger than twice any other. Specifically, the ratio of largest to smallest standard deviation is $2.25/1.61 = 1.40$, which is less than 2. Conditions are safe for use of ANOVA. **(b)** Calculations are provided:

$$\bar{x} = \frac{17 \times 6.47 + 17 \times 3.75 + 17 \times 4.05 + 17 \times 5.02}{68} = 4.8225$$

$$\text{MSG} = \frac{17(6.47 - 4.8225)^2 + 17(3.75 - 4.8225)^2 + 17(4.05 - 4.8225)^2 + 17(5.02 - 4.8225)^2}{4 - 1} = 25.502$$

$$\text{MSE} = \frac{(17-1)2.25^2 + (17-1)1.77^2 (17-1)1.61^2 + (17-1)1.80^2}{68 - 4} = 3.507$$

$$F = \frac{\text{MSG}}{\text{MSE}} = 7.272$$

(c) We have df = $4 - 1 = 3$ and $68 - 4 = 64$, so we refer to the F distribution with 3 and 64 degrees of freedom. $P = 0.0003$ (obtained using software). There is strong evidence that the mean status scores among the four groups studied are not equal—a conclusion consistent with the solution to Exercise 27.2.

27.15 (c) the means of several populations

27.17 (c) The alternate hypothesis for ANOVA is always that there is some difference in the means (but it does not specify the type of difference).

27.19 (a) $P = 0.026$, so we reject H_0 and conclude that there is a difference in mean breaking strength.

27.21 (a) This is the problem of multiple comparisons.

27.23 (c) We do not have three independent samples from three populations. **Note:** *Students may select choice (a) because 14.14/7.10 = 1.99 is quite close to 2. This might mean that they did not read all possible choices.)*

27.25 The populations are college students who might view the advertisement with an art image, college students who might view the advertisement with a non-art image, and college students who might view the advertisement with no image. The response variable is student evaluation of the advertisement on the 1–7 scale. We test the hypothesis $H_0 : \mu_1 = \mu_2 = \mu_3$ (all three groups have equal mean advertisement evaluation) versus $H_a :$ not all means are equal. There are $I = 3$ populations; the samples sizes are $n_1 = n_2 = n_3 = 39$, so there are $N = 39 + 39 + 39 = 117$ individuals in the total sample. There are then $I - 1 = 3 - 1 = 2$ and $N - I = 117 - 3 = 114$ df.

27.27 The response variable is hemoglobin A1c level. We have $I = 4$ populations; a control (sedentary) population, an aerobic exercise population, a resistance training population, and a combined aerobic and resistance training population. We test hypothesis $H_0 : \mu_1 = \mu_2 = \mu_3 = \mu_4$ (all four groups have equal mean hemoglobin A1c levels) versus $H_a :$ not all means are equal. Sample sizes are $n_1 = 41$, $n_2 = 73$, $n_3 = 72$, and $n_4 = 76$. Our total sample size is $N = 41 + 73 + 72 + 76 = 262$. We have $I - 1 = 4 - 1 = 3$ and $N - I = 262 - 4 = 258$ df.

27.29 (a) The graph suggests that emissions rise when a plant is attacked because the mean control emission rate is half the smallest of the other rates. **(b)** The null hypothesis is "all groups have the same mean emission rate." The alternative is "at least one group has a different mean emission rate." **(c)** The most important piece of additional information would be whether the data are sufficiently close to Normally

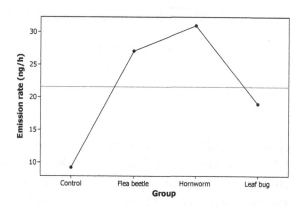

distributed. (From the description, it seems reasonably safe to assume that these are more or less random samples.) **(d)** The SEM $= s/\sqrt{8}$, so we can find the standard deviations by multiplying by $\sqrt{8}$; they are 16.77, 24.75, 18.78, and 24.38. However, this factor of $\sqrt{8}$ would cancel out in the process of finding the ratio of the largest and smallest standard deviations, so we can simply find this ratio directly from the SEM's: $\dfrac{8.75}{5.93} = \dfrac{24.75}{16.77} = 1.48$, which satisfies our rule of thumb that the largest sample standard deviation is no more than twice the smallest sample standard deviation.

27.31 (a) The stemplots are provided, and means and standard deviations are in the Minitab output. The means suggest that extra water in the spring has the greatest effect on biomass, with a lesser effect from added water in the winter. ANOVA is risky with these data; the standard deviation ratio is nearly 3 (58.77/21.69 = 2.71), and the winter and spring distributions may have skewness or outliers (although it is difficult to judge with such small samples).

```
Winter         Spring         Control
1              1              1 | 11
1              1              1 | 2
1 | 4          1              1 | 44
1 | 67         1              1 | 7
1 | 8          1              1 |
2              2              2 |
2              2              2 |
2              2              2 |
2 | 6          2              2 |
2 | 9          2 | 889        2 |
3              3 | 1          3 |
3              3 | 2          3 |
3              3              3 |
3              3              3 |
3              3 | 8          3 |
```

```
Level     N    Mean   StDev
control   6    136.65  21.69
spring    6    315.39  37.34
winter    6    205.17  58.77
```

(b) We wish to test whether the mean biomass from any group differs from the others: $H_0 : \mu_w = \mu_s = \mu_c$ (all treatments have the same mean) versus H_a: at least one mean is different. **(c)** ANOVA gives a statistically significant result ($F = 27.52$, df = 2 and 15, $P < 0.0005$), but as noted in part (a), the conditions for ANOVA are not satisfied. Based on the stemplots and the means, however, we should still be safe in concluding that added water increases biomass.

One-Way ANOVA: Biomass versus Treatment

```
Source      DF      SS      MS      F       P
Treatment    2    97583   48792   27.52   0.000
Error       15    26593    1773
Total       17   124176

S = 42.11    R-Sq = 78.58%    R-Sq(adj) = 75.73%
```

27.33 (a) STATE: Does sleep quality affect depression? PLAN: We have data on sleep quality and depression scores for 898 students at a large midwestern university. We'll have to assume these students are close to a random sample of college students and that the observations (students) are independent of one another. SOLVE: With such large sample sizes, we'll use side-by-side boxplots to examine the distributions. All three groups show outliers at the high end of the depression score range, but with such large samples (the smallest is 246), it is reasonable to believe the sample means have Normal distributions. The condition on standard deviations is satisfied because 4.719/2.560 = 1.84 < 2. We have $F = 75.52$ with df = 2 and 895, giving $P = 0.000$ (to three decimal places). CONCLUDE: The mean depression scores

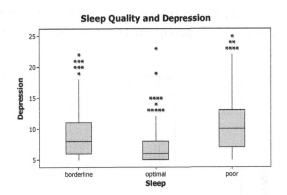

for the three levels of sleep quality are not the same. From the output and graphs, it appears the mean depression score for poor sleepers is highest; the mean depression score for optimal sleepers is lowest. **(b)** Assuming the students were randomly selected, the large sample size would lead us to believe these students are most likely representative of other college students. **(c)** Students were not randomly assigned to sleep conditions. Explanations about causation may vary, but this might well be a case of one condition (poor sleep) feeding the other (depression) in a "vicious cycle."

```
Source    DF        SS      MS       F      P
Sleep      2    2162.3  1081.1   72.52  0.000
Error    895   13343.7    14.9
Total    897   15506.0
                                 Individual 95% CIs For Mean Based on
                                 Pooled StDev
Level           N    Mean   StDev  -----+---------+---------+---------+----
borderline    246   8.764   3.892                    (---*---)
optimal       309   7.013   2.560  (--*---)
poor          343  10.656   4.719                                (---*--)
                                   -----+---------+---------+---------+----
                                      7.2       8.4       9.6      10.8
Pooled StDev = 3.861
```

27.35 STATE: Are the mean tip percentages constant for all types of weather forecasts (no forecast, good forecast, bad forecast)? **PLAN:** We will perform an ANOVA test for the equality of means. **SOLVE:** First, we see that the ratio of largest standard deviation to smallest standard deviation is $2.388/1.959 = 1.22$, which is less than 2. Histograms of the samples are provided. There is some evidence of non-Normality and perhaps one outlier in the "No Weather Report" group. We proceed, because the samples are reasonably large. From the output, we have $F = 20.679$ with $3 - 1 = 2$ and $60 - 3 = 57$ df, with $P = 0.000$. **CONCLUDE:** There is overwhelming evidence that the mean tip percentages are not the same for all three groups. Examination of the summary statistics and the histograms provided suggests that while the mean tip for the bad forecast group is similar to that of the no forecast group, the mean tip for the good forecast is higher.

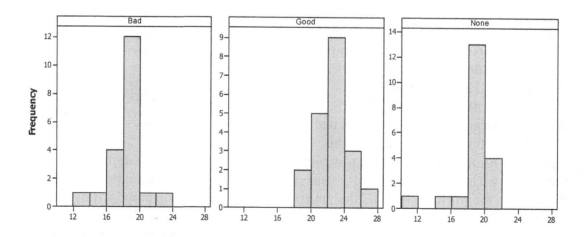

One-way ANOVA: Percent versus Report

```
Source   DF      SS     MS      F       P          Level   N    Mean   StDev
Report    2  192.22  96.11  20.68   0.000          Bad    20  18.180  2.098
Error    57  264.92   4.65                         Good   20  22.220  1.959
Total    59  457.15                                None   20  18.725  2.388

S = 2.156    R-Sq = 42.05%    R-Sq(adj) = 40.02%
```

27.37 (a) The table is given in the Minitab output below; because 4.500/3.529 = 1.28 < 2, ANOVA should be safe. The means suggest that logging reduces the number of species per plot and that recovery takes more than eight years. **(b)** ANOVA gives F = 6.02 with df = 2 and 30, so $P < 0.01$ (software gives 0.006). We conclude that these differences are significant; the mean number of species per plot really is lower in logged areas.

One-Way ANOVA: Species versus Group

```
Source   DF     SS      MS     F      P
Group     2  204.4  102.2   6.02  0.006
Error    30  509.2   17.0
Total    32  713.6

S = 4.120    R-Sq = 28.64%    R-Sq(adj) = 23.88%

                           Individual 95% CIs For Mean Based on
                           Pooled StDev
Level   N    Mean   StDev   ---------+---------+---------+---------+
1      12  17.500   3.529                     (-------*------)
2      12  11.750   4.372   (-------*-------)
3       9  13.667   4.500        (--------*--------)
                           ---------+---------+---------+---------+
                              12.0      15.0      18.0      21.0

Pooled StDev = 4.120
```

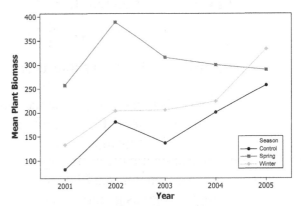

27.39 (a) See plot. **(b)** There is a slight increase in growth when water is added in the wet season, but there is a much greater increase when it is added during the dry season. **(c)** The means differ significantly during the first three years. **(d)** The year 2005 is the only one for which the winter biomass was higher than the spring biomass.

27.41 In addition to a high standard deviation ratio (117.18/35.57 = 3.29), the spring biomass distribution has a high outlier.

27.43 (a) This is a comparison of two means, so it requires a two-sample t test. **(b)** This is a comparison of three means, so it requires ANOVA. **(c)** This is a comparison of three proportions, so it requires a chi-square test of homogeneity.

27.45 is a Web-based exercise.

Chapter 28 – Nonparametric Tests

28.1 (a) The medians are 549.522 minutes (lean) and 388.8845 minutes (obese); the lean group appears to be more active. **(b)** See the table. **(c)** The Wilcoxon statistic is computed by summing the highlighted ranks in the table: $W = 3 + 7 + 13 + 14 + 15 + 16 + 17 + 18 + 19 + 20 = 142$. If H_0 is true, then $\mu_W = \frac{(10)(21)}{2} = 105$ and $\sigma_W = \sqrt{\frac{(10)(10)(21)}{12}} = 13.23$. **(d)** Our computed value of W is about $2.8\,\sigma_W$ above μ_W, providing reasonable evidence against H_0.

Group	Stand	Rank	Group	Stand	Rank
Obese	260.244	1	Obese	426.356	11
Obese	267.344	2	Obese	464.756	12
Lean	319.212	3	Lean	504.700	13
Obese	347.375	4	Lean	511.100	14
Obese	358.650	5	Lean	543.388	15
Obese	367.138	6	Lean	555.656	16
Lean	374.831	7	Lean	578.869	17
Obese	410.631	8	Lean	584.644	18
Obese	413.667	9	Lean	607.925	19
Obese	416.531	10	Lean	677.188	20

28.3 (a) We observed that $W = 142$, so for a one-sided alternative, we compute $P(W \geq 141.5)$. **(b)** $P(W \geq 141.5) = P\left(Z \geq \frac{141.5 - 105}{13.23}\right) = P(Z \geq 2.76) = 0.0029$. This is strong evidence that lean subjects spend more time standing and walking.

28.5 STATE: Is there good evidence that high-progress readers score higher than low-progress readers? **PLAN:** Compare the score distributions with a graph, and test H_0: scores for both groups are identically distributed versus H_a: high-progress children systematically score higher. **SOLVE:** A back-to-back stemplot (not shown) supports a suspicion that high-progress readers have higher scores. The low outlier in the high-progress group should make us hesitant to use t procedures, so the Wilcoxon test is a better choice. The stemplot makes it easy to determine the rankings for the high-progress scores: $W = 4 + 7 + 8 + 9 + 10 = 38$. Under H_0, $\mu_W = \frac{(5)(11)}{2} = 27.5$ and $\sigma_W = \sqrt{\frac{(5)(5)(11)}{12}} = 4.787$. The P-value is $P(W \geq 37.5) = P(Z \geq 2.09) = 0.0183$. **CONCLUDE:** There is significant evidence that high-progress readers score higher on Story 2.

Minitab output: Mann-Whitney (Wilcoxon Rank Sum) Confidence Interval and Test

```
high        N =   5     Median =       0.8000
low         N =   5     Median =       0.4900
Point estimate for ETA1-ETA2 is        0.2600
96.3 Percent C.I. for ETA1-ETA2 is  (0.0200,0.5199)
W = 38.0
Test of ETA1 = ETA2  vs.  ETA1 > ETA2 is significant at 0.0184
```

28.7 Minitab output following agrees (up to rounding error) with the *P*-value found in the solution to Exercise 28.3, using the Normal approximation with continuity correction.

Minitab output: Mann-Whitney (Wilcoxon Rank Sum) Test

```
LeanStd     N =  10     Median =       549.5
ObeseStd    N =  10     Median =       388.9
W = 142.0
Test of ETA1 = ETA2  vs.  ETA1 > ETA2 is significant at 0.0029
```

28.9 To compare means with a *t* test, the hypotheses are $H_0 : \mu_L = \mu_0$ versus $H_a : \mu_L > \mu_0$. To compare distributions with a Wilcoxon test, use H_0: median$_L$ = median$_0$ versus H_a: median$_L$ > median$_0$, as long as we believe the distributions have the same shape. Alternatively, test H_0: the two distributions are the same versus H_a: the distribution of lean standing times is systematically higher.

28.11 (a) For the Wilcoxon test, the hypotheses are H_0: the two distributions for perceived life expectancies are the same versus H_a: perceived life expectancies for men and women differ systematically. For the two-sample *t* test, the hypotheses are $H_0 : \mu_W = \mu_M$ versus $H_a : \mu_W \neq \mu_M$, where μ_W and μ_M represent the mean perceived life expectancies for women and men, respectively. **(b)** Sorting the life expectancies (denoting those associated with women in bold), we obtain –28, –23, **–20**, –20, **–19**, –19, **–15**, –14, –13, **–12**, **–10**, –8, –5. The two expectancies of –20 occupy the third and fourth positions in this list, so each is assigned rank 3.5. Similarly, each of the two values of –19 is assigned rank 5.5 since these expectancies occupy positions five and six. **(c)** We sum the ranks corresponding to women, though this choice is arbitrary. $W = 3.5 + 5.5 + 7 + 10 + 11 + 12 + 13 = 62$. Under H_0, $\mu_W = \dfrac{(7)(14)}{2} = 49$ and

$\sigma_W = \sqrt{\dfrac{(7)(6)(14)}{12}} = 7$. The *P*-value is then $2P(W \geq 61.5) = 2P\left(Z \geq \dfrac{61.5 - 49}{7}\right) = 2P(Z \geq 1.79) = 0.0734$. This *P*-value is fairly close to the result obtained using the two-sample *t* test.

28.13 (a) Back-to-back stemplot is provided. Deviations from Normality are hard to spot with such a small sample; no deviations are apparent here, although 0.00 may be a low outlier. **(b)** To test $H_0: \mu_1 = \mu_2$ versus $H_a: \mu_1 > \mu_2$, we find $\bar{x}_1 = 0.676$, $\bar{x}_2 = 0.406$, and $t = 2.059$, which gives $P = 0.0446$ (df = 5.5). We have fairly strong evidence that high-progress readers have higher mean scores. **(c)** We test H_0: scores for both groups are identically distributed versus H_a: high-progress children systematically score higher. We find that $W = 36$ and $P = 0.0473$ (or 0.0463 "adjusted for ties"; Minitab output below); we have strong evidence against the hypothesis of identical distributions. This is equivalent to the conclusion reached in part (b).

High		Low
	0	0
	1	
	2	
	3	6
	4	0
75	5	5
	6	
20	7	2
4	8	

```
Minitab output: Mann-Whitney (Wilcoxon Rank Sum) Test
HiProg1    N =   5    Median =      0.7000
LoProg1    N =   5    Median =      0.4000
W = 36.0
Test of ETA1 = ETA2  vs.  ETA1 > ETA2 is significant at 0.0473
The test is significant at 0.0463 (adjusted for ties)
```

28.15 PLAN: Compare the seed masses for the two groups of plants (with and without cicadas) graphically and numerically and using an appropriate test. SOLVE: See the solution to Exercise 7.46 for back-to-back stemplots and summary statistics. Both stemplots suggest that the two-sample t test might not be safe: The cicada stemplot has two possible outliers, and the control stemplot suggests possible non-Normality (it appears to have two peaks). We test H_0: seed masses for both groups are identically distributed versus H_a: cicada-group seed masses are systematically higher. We find that $W = 1567$ and $P = 0.0530$. CONCLUDE: We have fairly strong evidence that dead cicadas increase seed mass, although it is not quite significant at $\alpha = 0.05$.

```
Minitab output: Mann-Whitney (Wilcoxon Rank Sum) Test
cicada     N =  39    Median =     0.23800
control    N =  33    Median =     0.24100
W = 1567.0
Test of ETA1 = ETA2  vs.  ETA1 > ETA2 is significant at 0.0530
The test is significant at 0.0530 (adjusted for ties)
```

28.17 We do not have independent samples from two populations. Because each subject answered both questions, the samples are dependent.

28.19 (a) The distribution of differences is clearly skewed; with such a small sample, t procedures are not reliable. **(b)** One difference is 0, and the rest are positive, so taking absolute values has no effect. The 10 positive differences have ranks 1 through 10, so $W^+ = 1 + 2 + \ldots + 9 + 10 = 55$. **(c)** Under H_0, $\mu_{W^+} = \dfrac{(10)(11)}{4} = 27.5$ and

0	0012238
1	0
2	1
3	
4	
5	1
6	
7	0

$$\sigma_{W^+} = \sqrt{\frac{(10)(11)(21)}{24}} = 9.811.$$ Our observed value of W^+ is about 2.8 standard deviations above the mean, which suggests that the result is significant.

28.21 In the solution to Exercise 28.18, we found $P = 0.044$.

28.23 (a) The provided stemplot indicates left-skew; there are no outliers.
(b) Because all differences (observed – 78.1) are negative, the statistic value is $W^+ = 0$. This gives $P = 0.009$, so we reject H_0; there is strong evidence that the median is lower than 78.1%.

4	9
5	1
5	
5	4
5	
5	
6	0
6	33
6	445

Minitab output: Wilcoxon Signed Rank Test

```
TEST OF MEDIAN = 78.10 VERSUS MEDIAN N.E. 78.10
                     N FOR    WILCOXON              ESTIMATED
              N      TEST   STATISTIC   P-VALUE       MEDIAN
Nitrogen      9        9         0.0     0.009        59.65
```

28.25 (a) Considering sweetness rating changes, we test H_0: median = 0 versus H_a: median > 0. We find $W^+ = 47.5$ and $P = 0.023$, so we conclude that the cola does lose sweetness in storage. (See the note in the solution to Exercise 28.20 for an explanation of the estimated median reported by Minitab.) **(b)** The conclusions are the same, and the P-values are quite similar. The t-test hypotheses are H_0: $\mu_1 = \mu_2$ versus H_a: $\mu_1 > \mu_2$. Both tests assume that the tasters are an SRS of all tasters; the t test also assumes that the before-minus-after sweetness differences are Normally distributed.

Minitab output: Wilcoxon Signed Rank Test

```
TEST OF MEDIAN = 0.000000 VERSUS MEDIAN G.T.  0.000000
                     N FOR    WILCOXON              ESTIMATED
              N      TEST   STATISTIC   P-VALUE       MEDIAN
Loss         10       10        47.5     0.023        1.150
```

28.27 (a) Stemplots provided reveal a high outlier in the spring distribution. Means and standard deviations (in g/cm^2) are given with the stemplots; we also note that the standard deviation ratio is greater than 3. Both the means and the stemplots suggest that extra water in the spring has the greatest effect on biomass, with a lesser effect from added water in the winter. **(b)** ANOVA tests H_0: $\mu_w = \mu_s = \mu_c$ versus H_a: at least one mean is different. Kruskal-Wallis tests H_0: the three distributions are the same versus H_a: biomass is systematically higher in some group(s). **(c)** There are $I = 3$ populations, with $n_1 = n_2 = n_3 = 6$ in each sample, for a total sample size of $N = 18$. Ranked measurements are shown in the table. **(d)** The three rank sums are $R_c = 37$, $R_w = 56$, and $R_s = 78$. The Kruskal-Wallis statistic is therefore

$$H = \frac{12}{(18)(19)}\left(\frac{37^2}{6} + \frac{56^2}{6} + \frac{78^2}{6}\right) - 3(19) = 4.92 \text{ with df} = I - 1 = 2. \text{ Table D yields } 0.05 < P <$$

0.10, in close agreement with the Minitab output provided. The data give very weak evidence that the distributions are not all the same.

	Winter	Spring	Control
	$\bar{x} = 223.6$	299.5	201.1
	$s = 35.6$	117.2	39.2
	1	1	1 | 3
	1 | 5	1	1 | 7
	2 | 123	2 | 114	2 | 0134
	2 | 55	2 | 7	2
	3	3 | 4	3
	3	3	3
	4	4	4
	4	4	4
	5	5 | 1	5

Group	Biomass	Rank	Group	Biomass	Rank
C	134.985	1	C	231.764	10
W	158.667	2	W	233.816	11
C	178.999	3	S	240.193	12
C	205.516	4	C	242.680	13
W	212.323	5	W	253.451	14
C	212.486	6	W	254.645	15
S	212.532	7	S	270.578	16
S	213.988	8	S	342.283	17
W	228.588	9	S	517.665	18

```
Minitab output: Kruskal-Wallis Test
LEVEL     NOBS      MEDIAN  AVE. RANK    Z VALUE
    1         6       231.2        9.3      -0.09
    2         6       255.4       13.0       1.97
    3         6       209.0        6.2      -1.87
OVERALL      18                    9.5

H = 4.92   d.f. = 2   p = 0.086
```

28.29 PLAN: We use the Kruskal-Wallis procedure to test the hypotheses H_0: all medians are equal versus H_a: at least one median is different. SOLVE: The four medians are 126, 126, 131, and 110 pounds. The Kruskal-Wallis test gives $H = 5.35$, df = 3, and $P = 0.149$. CONCLUDE: We do not have enough evidence to conclude that breaking strength differs for varying lengths of burial.

Note: ANOVA is not appropriate for comparing these four groups because of the large differences in the standard deviations, ranging from 4.60 lb for the 2-week sample to 16.087 lb for the 16-week sample.

28.31 For the Kruskal-Wallis test, we need two or more independent samples. Because these data come from different questions being asked of the same people, the responses are not independent. (We have several variables measured from a single group, rather than a single variable measured for several different groups.)

28.33 (a) We have two independent samples, so the Wilcoxon rank sum test is appropriate.

28.35 (b) The control group emissions are ranked 6, 8, 5, 4, 1, and 2, so $W = 26$.

28.37 (b) The altered data creates two ties; the new ranks for the control group are now 6.5, 8, 4.5, 3, 1, and 2.

28.39 (a) The mean is $\mu_{W^+} = \dfrac{(10)(10+1)}{4} = 44.5$.

28.41 (b) There are three groups being compared, so df = $I - 1 = 3 - 1 = 2$.

28.43 PLAN: We use the Kruskal-Wallis procedure to test H_0: all four lightness distributions are the same versus H_a: some distribution is different. SOLVE: Side-by-side stemplots reveal some skewness as well as a possible high outlier with Method C and two low outliers with Method B; medians are listed in the Minitab output below. The Kruskal-Wallis test statistic is $H = 22.35$ with df = 3, for which $P < 0.0005$. CONCLUDE: The observed differences are significant. In particular, it appears that Method B typically yields the darkest results, and Method C yields the lightest results.

Method A		Method B		Method C		Method D	
40		40	89	40		40	
41	1	41		41		41	
41	2	41	2233	41		41	
41	44	41	5	41		41	
41	7	41	6	41		41	667
41	8	41		41		41	99
42	0	42		42		42	0
42	2	42		42	223	42	23
42		42		42	445	42	
42		42		42	6	42	
42		42		42		42	
42		42		42		42	
43		43		43	1	43	

Minitab output: Kruskal-Wallis Test

LEVEL	NOBS	MEDIAN	AVE. RANK	Z VALUE
A	8	41.61	13.0	-1.22
B	8	41.29	6.6	-3.46
C	8	42.44	27.9	3.98
D	8	41.98	18.5	0.70
OVERALL	32		16.5	

```
H = 22.35  d.f. = 3  p = 0.000
H = 22.36  d.f. = 3  p = 0.000 (adjusted for ties)
```

28.45 PLAN: We have two independent samples. We compare the distributions of weight losses for each group, then decide on an appropriate analysis for determining whether gastric banding results in greater weight loss than lifestyle intervention. SOLVE: Histograms for each sample are provided. Weight losses appear to be generally greater in the gastric-banding group but skew in the lifestyle-intervention group, suggesting that a Wilcoxon rank sum test is appropriate. From the output, $W = 697$ and $P = 0.000002$. CONCLUDE: There is overwhelming evidence that the median weight loss for patients using gastric banding is greater than that of patients using a lifestyle intervention.

Mann-Whitney Test and CI: Banding, Lifestyle

```
            N  Median
Banding    24   33.35
Lifestyle  18    1.70


Point estimate for ETA1-ETA2 is 31.75
95.1 Percent CI for ETA1-ETA2 is (22.30,40.60)
W = 697.0
Test of ETA1 = ETA2 vs ETA1 > ETA2 is significant at 0.0000
The test is significant at 0.0000 (adjusted for ties)
```

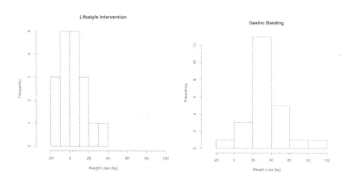

28.47 PLAN: Consider the differences sfair − sfast. We test the hypotheses H_0: median = 0 versus H_a: median ≠ 0; the two-sided alternative means "ratings for fairs and fast food restaurants are systematically different in some way." SOLVE: We find $\bar{x}$ = 0.0693 and M = 0. Applying the Wilcoxon signed rank test to these differences, we find W^+ = 4730.5 and P = 0.206. CONCLUDE: The difference in safety ratings is not significant. (The large number of ties is not a cause for concern in this case. Ties can lead to a bias in favor of H_a, but even with this advantage for the alternative, the evidence was not convincing.)

```
Minitab output: Wilcoxon Signed Rank Test
TEST OF MEDIAN = 0.000000 VERSUS MEDIAN N.E. 0.000000

                N FOR   WILCOXON            ESTIMATED
          N     TEST   STATISTIC  P-VALUE    MEDIAN
Diffs    303    129     4730.5     0.206    0.000E+00
```

28.49 PLAN: The distribution of differences was examined in Chapter 20. Considering the difference in performance (VIG Fund minus EAFE), we test H_0: median = 0 versus H_a: median ≠ 0, taking a two-sided alternative because the VIG Fund could outperform or underperform the benchmark. SOLVE: The Wilcoxon signed rank test gives W^+ = 39.5 and P = 0.4258. CONCLUDE: We have very little reason to doubt that the median difference is 0; VIG Fund performance is not significantly different from its benchmark.

28.51 PLAN: We examine the within-stream minus upstream differences for the 13 tributaries, and test H_0: same richness distribution for both locations versus H_a: richness is systematically higher within tributaries. SOLVE: There are three negative differences (ranks 1.5, 8.5, and 12); the sum of the ranks of the positive differences is W^+ = 69, for which P = 0.054. CONCLUDE: There is evidence that richness is higher within tributaries than upstream from them, but the evidence is not very strong. In particular, it falls just short of being significant at the 5% level.

Note: The researchers actually used the binomial sign test, which is appropriate for matched pairs situations like this. This test is not presented in this text.

```
-1 | 1
-0 | 5
-0 | 1
 0 | 122334
 0 | 579
 1 | 3
```

Minitab output: Wilcoxon Signed Rank Test

```
TEST OF MEDIAN = 0.000000 VERSUS MEDIAN G.T. 0.000000

                 N FOR  WILCOXON              ESTIMATED
           N     TEST   STATISTIC  P-VALUE    MEDIAN
diff       13    13     69.0       0.054      3.000
```

28.53 is a Web-based exercise.

Chapter 29 – Multiple Regression

29.1 The model would be $\hat{y} = \beta_0 + \beta_1 x_1 + \beta_2 x_2$, where:

• β_0 is the intercept (the number of new birds for the first species when there are no returning birds).

• β_2 is the amount that the intercept differs for the second species (i.e., $\beta_0 + \beta_2$ is the number of new birds for the second species when there are no returning birds).

• β_1 is the slope—the rate at which the number of new birds changes in response to changes in the percent of returning birds.

29.3 With x representing the reporting date and y representing the percent reporting for jury duty, the slope and intercept for the simple regression model $\mu_y = \beta_0 + \beta_1 x$ are $b_1 = r\dfrac{s_y}{s_x}$ and $b_0 = \bar{y} - b_1\bar{x}$.

(a) For 1985, $b_1 = 0.399 \cdot \dfrac{4.537}{7.65} = 0.2366$ and $b_0 = 22.135 - b_1 \cdot 13.50 = 18.94$.

(b) For 1997, $b_1 = 0.707 \cdot \dfrac{17.94}{7.65} = 1.6580$ and $b_0 = 48.10 - b_1 \cdot 13.50 = 25.72$.

(c) For 1985 reporting dates, the slope tells us that as coded reporting date increases, the percent reporting for jury duty increases; specifically, that percent increases by about 0.2366 for each unit increase in reporting date (a two-week period). For 1997 reporting dates, the rate of increase is much greater: about 1.6580 percentage points for each unit change in reporting date. **(d)** The slopes are quite different. (This is also evident from the scatterplot.) **(e)** Considering the difference in the computed slopes and the appearance of the scatterplot, a multiple regression model with equal slopes seems inappropriate for this setting.

29.5 With x representing the reporting date and y representing the percent reporting for jury duty, the slope and intercept for the simple regression model $\mu_y = \beta_0 + \beta_1 x$ are $b_1 = r\dfrac{s_y}{s_x}$ and $b_0 = \bar{y} - b_1\bar{x}$.

(a) For 2003, $b_1 = -0.068\left(\dfrac{7.00}{7.65}\right) = -0.0622$ and $b_0 = 89.06 - b_1(13.50) = 89.90$.

(b) For 2004, $b_1 = 0.094\left(\dfrac{4.772}{7.65}\right) = 0.0586$ and $b_0 = 86.761 - b_1(13.50) = 85.97$.

(c) For 2003 reporting dates, the average percent reporting for jury duty decreases by 0.0622 for each unit increase in reporting date. For 2004 reporting dates, the average percent reporting increases by 0.0586 for each unit increase in reporting date. **(d)** The slopes are fairly similar—one is negative and one is positive, but both are rather close to 0. Over 26 two-week periods, the percent reporting changes by −1.6% (2003 slope) or +1.5% (2004 slope); both of those changes are small relative to the intercept. **(e)** Because the slopes are similar, a multiple regression model with equal slopes would appear to be acceptable in this case. (Note, however, that there is some suggestion in the scatterplot that the 2003 scatter might be greater than the 2004 scatter.) **(f)** The slopes in 1998 and 2000 (−0.668 and −0.766, respectively) are substantially greater (more negative) than the 2003 slope. **(g)** The commissioner should be quite happy. His modifications appear to have had two positive results: More potential jurors are reporting (all percents in 2003 and 2004 are greater than 75%), and there is less variation over the course of the year (the slopes are close to 0).

29.7 (a) The regression formula is $\hat{y} = 18.1 - 5.41x_1 + 0.848x_2$. **(b)** Because $b_2 = 0.848$ is positive, we can conclude that nestling mass was higher for exposed nests. (This might not have been true for all nests, but it holds on average.) **(c)** The regression standard error is $s = 1.01583$; this is our estimate of the degree of scatter about the regression function. **(d)** The squared multiple correlation coefficient is "R-sq" in the Minitab output: $R^2 = 47.7\% = 0.477$. This tells us that the regression function explains about 47.7% of the variation in nestling mass.

29.9 (a) The 95% confidence interval is $b_1 \pm t^* \mathrm{SE}_{b_1}$, where $b_1 = 0.69828$, $\mathrm{SE}_{b_1} = 0.02628$, and $t^* = 1.984$ (from Table C with df = 100), 1.9715 (from software with df = 206), or 1.96 (for students who use a Normal distribution). This gives 0.6461 to 0.7504, 0.6465 to 0.7501, or 0.6468 to 0.7498. **(b)** Use the same interval: Under this model, the lines are parallel, so the slope is the same. **(c)** Both $\frac{2}{3}$ and $\frac{3}{4}$ should be in both intervals. (For students who used $t^* = 1.96$, $\frac{3}{4}$ is barely outside the interval.)

(d) Compared to the interval in the previous exercise, this interval has a larger margin of error and is lower (the upper limit of this interval is less than the lower limit of the previous interval). **(e)** To test this hypothesis against a two-sided alternative, we take $t = \dfrac{b - 2/3}{\mathrm{SE}_b} = \dfrac{0.69828 - 2/3}{0.02628} = 1.20$. This value of t is clearly too small to be significant (software tells us that $P = 0.2304$, so we have little reason to doubt that β differs from $\frac{2}{3}$). **(f)** Now, $t = \dfrac{b - 3/4}{\mathrm{SE}_b} = \dfrac{0.69828 - 3/4}{0.02628} = -1.97$, and $P = 0.0504$. This is fairly strong evidence that β is different from $\frac{3}{4}$, although it is not quite significant at the 5% level.

Note: Of course, our interval from part (a)—and specifically, the observation made in part (c)—told us that the tests in (e) and (f) would not be significant.

29.11 The model is $\mu_y = \beta_0 + \beta_1 x_1 + \beta_2 x_2 + \beta_3 x_1 x_2$. β_0 and β_1 are the intercept and slope for the first species (when $x_2 = 0$), and ($\beta_0 + \beta_2$) and ($\beta_1 + \beta_3$) are the intercept and slope for the other species (when $x_2 = 1$).

29.13 The realistic restriction (time $= y = 0$ when $x_1 = 0$) means that the intercept β_0 of our model should be 0. Recalling the algebra formula distance = rate · time, we note that a trip of x_1 miles at speed s mph takes x_1/s hours. Therefore, we need a line with slope $\dfrac{1}{20}$ for buses, and a line with slope $\dfrac{1}{28}$ for autos. If x_2 is the indicator of transportation type (0 for bus, 1 for auto), then the model is

$$\mu_y = \frac{1}{20}x_1 + \left(\frac{1}{28} - \frac{1}{20}\right)x_1 x_2 = \frac{1}{20}x_1 - \frac{1}{70}x_1 x_2.$$ If x_2 is the other way around (1 for bus, 0 for auto), then the model is $\mu_y = \dfrac{1}{28}x_1 + \left(\dfrac{1}{20} - \dfrac{1}{28}\right)x_1 x_2 = \dfrac{1}{28}x_1 + \dfrac{1}{70}x_1 x_2$.

29.15 (a) Both men (squares) and women (circles) show fairly steady improvement. Women have made more rapid progress, but their progress seems to have slowed, while men's records may be dropping more rapidly in recent years. **(b)** The two regression formulas are

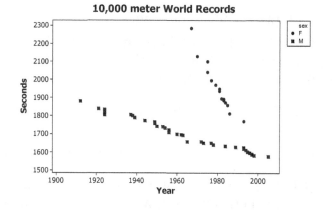

Men: $\hat{R} = 8124.1 - 3.271\,\text{Year}$

Women: $\hat{R} = 41373 - 19.90\,\text{Year}$

These can be found as two separate regressions (one for men and one for women), or as a multiple regression model with an indicator variable for sex and an interaction term. **(c)** The data support the first claim (the women's line is much steeper) but do not seem to support the second.

Note: Exercise 29.26 calls for the ANOVA table for the multiple regression; check whether your software will perform this computation before assigning this exercise.

```
The regression equation is
record = 41373 - 19.9 year - 33249 sex_M + 16.6 Male*Yr

Predictor        Coef  SE Coef        T       P
Constant        41373     1714    24.14   0.000
year         -19.9046   0.8654   -23.00   0.000
sex_M          -33249     1734   -19.17   0.000
Male*Yr       16.6339   0.8761    18.99   0.000

S = 21.1788    R-Sq = 98.3%    R-Sq(adj) = 98.2%
```

29.17 The model is $\mu_{\sqrt{y}} = \beta_0 + \beta_1 x + \beta_2 x^2$. Students might try to express the model in terms of y rather than $\sqrt{y}$, but that overcomplicates the model: It means squaring the quadratic expression to obtain a fourth degree polynomial, in which the five coefficients are derived from the three coefficients in the model above.

29.19 (a) Scatterplot is shown. **(b)** The quadratic regression equation gives the estimated mean response at time t: $\mu_{\text{count}} = 2002.9 - 5.2725t + 0.003180t^2$ (Minitab output below). **(c)** The quadratic model does a poor job of approximating the points of the scatterplot and is therefore a poor choice for prediction. **(d)** This scatterplot is on the right. **(e)** Regressing the natural logarithm of the counts on time gives the line LogCount = 7.3767 − 0.004521t. This line is shown on the second scatterplot below. A stemplot of the residuals and a plot of residuals versus fitted values are also shown. **(f)** The linear fit to transformed counts is certainly better than the quadratic model, but the residual plots show that it is far from perfect.

```
 -5 | 431
 -4 | 7
 -3 | 988430
 -2 | 88654322210
 -1 | 999888777655555433333322221111110000
 -0 | 998777776555443333333333222111110
  0 | 0024666
  1 | 14468
  2 | 01226678
  3 | 049
  4 | 0449
  5 | 26
  6 | 4678
  7 | 0
  8 | 3
  9 | 8
 10 |
 11 | 4
```

Minitab output: Quadratic model

The regression equation is count = 2003 - 5.27 seconds + 0.00318 secsqd

Predictor	Coef	Stdev	t-ratio	p
Constant	2002.9	115.6	17.33	0.000
seconds	-5.2725	0.4196	-12.57	0.000
secsqd	0.0031798	0.0003204	9.92	0.000

Linear model on transformed data

The regression equation is logcnt = 7.38 - 0.00452 seconds

Predictor	Coef	Stdev	t-ratio	p
Constant	7.37666	0.05482	134.56	0.000
seconds	-0.00452103	0.00007520	-60.12	0.000

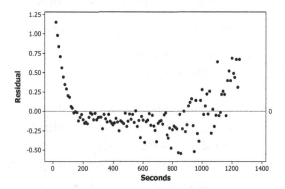

29.21 (a) Body fat y and waist size x_1 should be positively correlated because large (small) values of one variable tend to go with large (small) values of the other; that is, people with high (low) body fat will typically have larger (smaller) waists. **(b)** In general, among men with the same waist size but different amounts of body fat, we would expect taller men to have lower body fat. (For example, we expect a 6-foot 6-inch man with a 40-inch waist to be carrying less fat than a 5-foot 6-inch man with the same waist size.) **(c)** With both variables in the model, we would expect the coefficient of height (x_2) to be negative because the presence of waist size (x_1) would allow the model to give separate predictions for men of varying heights with a fixed waist size, as was discussed in part (b).

29.23 (a) The regression equation is $\hat{P} = -28408 + 766\text{DEPTH} - 3.23\ \text{DEPTH}^2$. **(b)** For this model, $R^2 = 4.7\%$—much smaller than the 92.6% for the quadratic model based on the carat weight of the diamond. While this exercise did not ask for a scatterplot, the one provided clearly illustrates that there is little association between these variables; no model using only depth could predict price well.

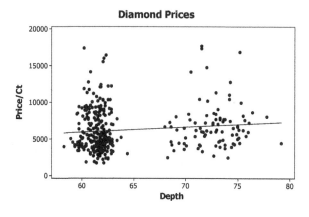

29.25 (a) The regression equation is in the first Minitab output below. **(b)** This model explains $R^2 = 93.7\%$ of the variation in weight. **(c)** The ANOVA table ($F = 396.10$, $P < 0.0005$) gives strong evidence that at least one of β_1 and β_2 is not zero. **(d)** The t tests ($t = 2.53$ and $P = 0.014$ for length, $t = 3.75$ and $P < 0.0005$ for width) suggest that both coefficients are not zero. **(e)** The new regression equation is in the second Minitab output below. **(f)** This model explains $R^2 = 98.5\%$ of the variation in weight. **(g)** The ANOVA table ($F = 1114.68$, $P < 0.0005$) gives strong evidence that at least one of the three coefficients is not zero. **(h)** With the addition of an interaction term to the model, the coefficient of length is not significantly different from 0 ($t = -1.10$, $P = 0.274$). In fact, the intercept is also not significantly different from 0 ($t = 1.94$, $P = 0.058$). Furthermore, the estimated coefficients of both length and width change from positive to negative when the interaction term is added.

Minitab output: length and width

```
The regression equation is
   weight = - 579 + 14.3 length + 113 width
```

Predictor	Coef	Stdev	t-ratio	p
Constant	-578.76	43.67	-13.25	0.000
length	14.307	5.659	2.53	0.014
width	113.50	30.26	3.75	0.000

```
s = 88.68      R-sq = 93.7%    R-sq(adj) = 93.5%
```

Analysis of Variance

SOURCE	DF	SS	MS	F	p
Regression	2	6229333	3114666	396.10	0.000
Error	53	416762	7863		
Total	55	6646094			

length, width, and length*width

```
The regression equation is
   weight = 114 - 3.48 length - 94.6 width + 5.24 interact
```

Predictor	Coef	Stdev	t-ratio	p
Constant	113.93	58.78	1.94	0.058
length	-3.483	3.152	-1.10	0.274
width	-94.63	22.30	-4.24	0.000
interact	5.2412	0.4131	12.69	0.000

```
s = 44.24      R-sq = 98.5%    R-sq(adj) = 98.4%
```

Analysis of Variance

SOURCE	DF	SS	MS	F	p
Regression	3	6544329	2181443	1114.68	0.000
Error	52	101765	1957		
Total	55	6646094			

29.27 Shown below are the Minitab fits, confidence intervals, and prediction intervals for the first 10 fish, using the second model found in Exercise 29.25. (The Minitab command used to produce these intervals also produced results for the other 46 fish, but they are not shown here.) These intervals were created using a t distribution with df = 52. In particular, for the tenth fish, the fitted value is 84.02 g. We are 95% confident that the mean weight of all such fish (length 21 cm, width 2.8 cm) is between 63.12 and 104.91 g, and we are 95% confident that an individual fish would weigh between −7.20 and 175.23 g. (The lower limit of the prediction interval is nonsense, so we should report it as 0 g.)

Minitab output

```
   Fit  Stdev.Fit      95.0% C.I.            95.0% P.I.
  15.38     29.05   ( -42.94,  73.69)   ( -90.85, 121.60) XX
  27.57     17.30   (  -7.15,  62.29)   ( -67.77, 122.91)
  32.36     13.64   (   4.97,  59.75)   ( -60.56, 125.28)
  42.38     11.74   (  18.83,  65.93)   ( -49.48, 134.24)
  56.27     10.04   (  36.11,  76.42)   ( -34.78, 147.32)
  66.87     11.12   (  44.55,  89.19)   ( -24.68, 158.42)
  68.22      9.38   (  49.40,  87.05)   ( -22.54, 158.99)
  78.44      8.49   (  61.39,  95.48)   ( -11.98, 168.85)
  84.66      8.58   (  67.44, 101.87)   (  -5.79, 175.10)
  84.02     10.41   (  63.12, 104.91)   (  -7.20, 175.23)
...
XX denotes a row with very extreme X values
```

29.29 Both scatterplots suggest nonconstant standard deviation: The residuals are more widely scattered for large values of Purchase12 and for small values of Recency.

29.31 (a) There are four parameters (a constant term, and the coefficients of MPH, IndSlow, and Incline).

29.33 (b) This is "S = 33.9422" in the Minitab output.

29.35 (a) Use the regression formula with IndSlow = 0 and Incline = 0.

29.37 (b) β_1 is the coefficient of MPH in the model (estimated to be 145.84). "More calories are burned for higher speeds" means that this coefficient is positive.

29.39 (a) Use the prediction interval (labeled "PI") given in the Minitab output, because we are estimating calories burned for one particular run on the treadmill.

29.41 (a) The model is $\mu_y = \beta_0 + \beta_1$ DIST $+ \beta_2$ HAND $+ \beta_3$ DIST*HAND, where HAND is an indicator variable for which hand is being used (either 1 for right and 0 for left or vice versa). In this model, β_0 and β_1 are the intercept and slope for one hand (when HAND = 0), while $\beta_0 + \beta_2$ and $\beta_1 + \beta_3$ are the intercept and slope, respectively, for the other hand (when HAND = 1). **(b)** The equation is given in the Minitab output below (where hand = 1 for right hand); this model explains $R^2 = 59.8\%$ of the variation in time. **(c)** The two equations for predicted time ($\hat{T}$) are $\hat{T} = 171.55 + 0.2619$ DIST for the left hand, and $\hat{T} = (171.55 - 72.18) + (0.2619 - 0.2336)$ DIST $= 99.37 + 0.0283$ DIST for the right hand. In the accompanying scatterplot, right-hand points are shown as squares, while left-hand points are shown as dots.

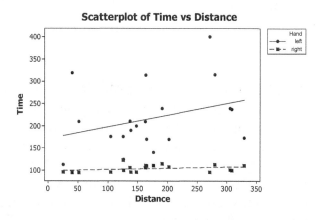
Scatterplot of Time vs Distance

Minitab output

```
The regression equation is
    time = 172 + 0.262 distance - 72.2 hand - 0.234 dist*hand

Predictor        Coef       Stdev     t-ratio        p
Constant       171.55       25.25        6.79    0.000
distance       0.2619      0.1308        2.00    0.053
hand           -72.18       35.71       -2.02    0.051
dist*hand     -0.2336      0.1850       -1.26    0.215

s = 50.61      R-sq = 59.8%      R-sq(adj) = 56.4%

Analysis of Variance

SOURCE        DF          SS          MS        F       p
Regression     3      136949       45650    17.82    0.000
Error         36       92198        2561
Total         39      229146
```

29.43 (a) In the scatterplot provided, squares correspond to Redding and filled circles correspond to Pasadena. **(b)** A parallel slopes model would not be reasonable because over time Pasadena's mean temperature appears to have increased at a faster rate than that for Redding. **(c)** The model appropriate for testing the hypothesis that the slope of the regression line for Redding is equal to the slope of the regression line for Pasadena is $\mu_y = \beta_0 + \beta_1 \text{Year} + \beta_2 \text{Ind\_Pas} + \beta_3 \text{Ind\_Pas*Year}$, where the variable Ind_Pas is an indicator variable (1 for Pasadena, 0 for Redding). We test $H_0: \beta_3 = 0$ versus $H_a: \beta_3 \neq 0$, yielding $t = 3.64$ and $P < 0.0005$. There is overwhelming evidence against H_0, suggesting that the parallel slopes model is not suitable. **(d)** Inferences here are at best barely reasonable. The residual plot suggests no systematic nonlinearity in the fit, although there is an extreme outlier corresponding to 2005's Pasadena temperature. A histogram of the residuals is slightly skewed.

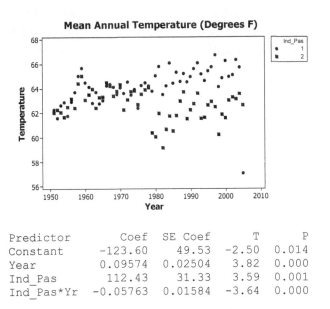

```
Predictor          Coef    SE Coef        T        P
Constant        -123.60      49.53    -2.50    0.014
Year            0.09574    0.02504     3.82    0.000
Ind_Pas          112.43      31.33     3.59    0.001
Ind_Pas*Yr     -0.05763    0.01584    -3.64    0.000
```

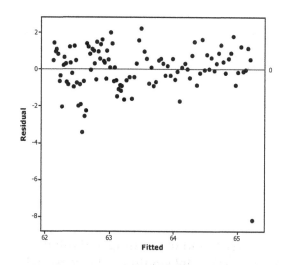

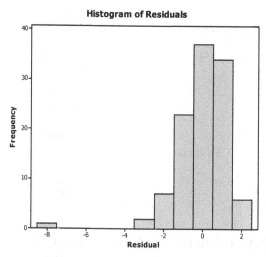

29.45 (a) The scatterplot is provided. **(b)** The two regression lines are

$\hat{G} = 1.1755 + 0.16768\ \text{DegDay}$ for nonwinter months, and

$\hat{G} = 1.4778 + 0.18061\ \text{DegDay}$ for winter months. **(c)** Based on the appearance of the scatterplot (both sets of points appear to fall in the same linear pattern) and the final two coefficients in the Minitab

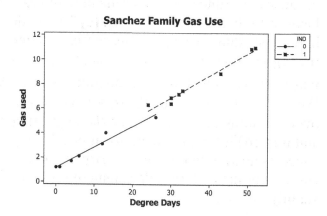

output (which are not significantly different from 0), one regression line would be sufficient. (Indeed, regression with DegDay as the only explanatory variable gives R^2 = 99.1% and s = 0.3389, which are similar to the results for this multiple regression model.)

```
Minitab output
The regression equation is
   gas = 1.18 + 0.168 DegDay + 0.302 IndWinter + 0.0129 dd*winter

Predictor      Coef      Stdev    t-ratio        p
Constant     1.1755     0.1523       7.72    0.000
DegDay       0.16768    0.01334     12.57    0.000
IndWinter    0.3023     0.4619       0.65    0.525
dd*winter    0.01293    0.01757      0.74    0.476

s = 0.3161     R-sq = 99.3%     R-sq(adj) = 99.1%
```

29.47 (a) The points in this scatterplot are so close together that it is difficult to distinguish between them in the lower left. **(b)** The coefficients for this model are given in the Minitab output below. **(c)** The model fits the data well (R^2 = 98.6%, s = 49.98). We note that the coefficient of IndSlow is not significantly different from 0, so it might be dropped from the model. **(d)** The coefficient of the Treadmill indicator variable is significantly different from 0, so there is a difference between the two treadmills. Specifically, we estimate that users of the Cybex treadmill burn about 26.2 fewer calories per hour, on the average.

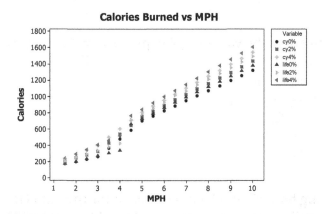

Minitab output

```
The regression equation is
  calories = 42.7 + 154 mph - 27.3 Ind_slow - 148 NoIncline - 73.7 2%Incline
            - 26.2 Treadmill

Predictor      Coef      Stdev    t-ratio        p
Constant      42.72      20.63       2.07    0.041
mph         153.566      2.676      57.38    0.000
Ind_slow     -27.33      16.70      -1.64    0.105
NoIncline   -147.89      11.78     -12.55    0.000
2%Incline    -73.69      11.78      -6.26    0.000
Treadmill   -26.204      9.619      -2.72    0.008

s = 49.98       R-sq = 98.6%      R-sq(adj) = 98.6%
```

29.49 (a) The outlier is student #55, who had the lowest GPA (0.530) but moderate values of the three explanatory variables (IQ = 103, c2 = 10, and c5 = 5—all three values are near the first quartile for these three variables). This might be spotted in your software's regression output or by examining the residuals (this observation had a residual of about -5.8, while $s = 1.5$, so it was nearly 4 standard deviations below 0). **(b)** The point identified as influential might vary among software packages; the version of Minitab used for these solutions produced the list below, and these points are marked with crosses in the scatterplot.

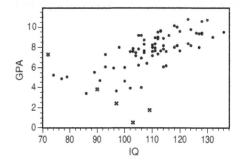

Minitab output: Regression diagnostics

```
Unusual Observations
Obs.        iq        gpa      Fit   Stdev.Fit    Residual   St.Resid
  8         97      2.412    6.205       0.313      -3.793      -2.59R
 22        109      1.760    5.220       0.595      -3.460      -2.51RX
 51        103      0.530    6.326       0.244      -5.796      -3.92R
 54         72      7.295    4.703       0.696       2.592       1.95 X
 72         90      3.820    4.834       0.723      -1.014      -0.77 X
```

(c) Regression using only the variable c2 explains r^2 = 36.1% of the variation in GPA.

Minitab output: Model using c2 only

```
The regression equation is gpa = 3.31 + 0.330 c2

Predictor       Coef       Stdev     t-ratio        p
Constant      3.3060      0.6603        5.01    0.000
c2            0.33023     0.05041       6.55    0.000

s = 1.689      R-sq = 36.1%      R-sq(adj) = 35.3%
```

(d) Regression using both c2 and IQ is a better fit for the data (R^2 = 49.4%), and the coefficient of c2 is still significantly nonzero (t = 3.70, P < 0.0005), indicating that the predictive value of c2 does not completely overlap with that of IQ.

Minitab output: Model using c2 and IQ

```
The regression equation is gpa = - 2.61 + 0.199 c2 + 0.0694 iq

Predictor       Coef       Stdev     t-ratio        p
Constant     -2.613       1.459       -1.79    0.077
c2            0.19935     0.05394       3.70    0.000
iq            0.06941     0.01564       4.44    0.000

s = 1.514      R-sq = 49.4%      R-sq(adj) = 48.0%
```

(e) Using the IQ and c2 model, the predicted GPA is $\hat{G}$ = −2.61 + 0.199(14) + 0.0694(115) = 8.16.

29.51 (a) Students might fit a model with or without interaction; both are shown. The regression equation is $\widehat{SellingPrice}$ = 135.21204 + 1.20768 Appraisal − 0.29191 Month without the interaction and $\widehat{SellingPrice}$ = 53.48397 + 1.31934 Appraisal + 0.9841 Month − 0.001745 Month*Appraisal with the interaction. **(b)** The coefficient of multiple determination is R^2—either 58.0% or 58.2%, depending on which model was used. Either model explains only about 58% of the variation in selling price. **(c)** The regression standard error is either 223.471 or 225.582. Notice that the estimate of s is larger in the model with interaction, indicating a slightly worse fit.

Summary of Fit

RSquare	0.580053
RSquare Adj	0.560964
Root Mean Square Error	223.4709
Mean of Response	1046.277
Observations (or Sum Wgts)	47

Analysis of Variance

Source	DF	Sum of Squares	Mean Square	F Ratio
Model	2	3035060.5	1517530	30.3875
Error	44	2197327.0	49939	**Prob > F**
C. Total	46	5232387.4		<.0001*

Parameter Estimates

Term	Estimate	Std Error	t Ratio	Prob>|t|
Intercept	135.21204	138.511	0.98	0.3343
appraised	1.2076805	0.155592	7.76	<.0001*
month	-0.291906	0.76346	-0.38	0.7040

Summary of Fit

RSquare	0.581807
RSquare Adj	0.55263
Root Mean Square Error	225.5819
Mean of Response	1046.277
Observations (or Sum Wgts)	47

Analysis of Variance

Source	DF	Sum of Squares	Mean Square	F Ratio
Model	3	3044237.8	1014746	19.9411
Error	43	2188149.6	50887	**Prob > F**
C. Total	46	5232387.4		<.0001*

Parameter Estimates

Term	Estimate	Std Error	t Ratio	Prob>|t|
Intercept	53.483974	237.879	0.22	0.8232
appraised	1.3193397	0.306269	4.31	<.0001*
month	0.9841034	3.101953	0.32	0.7526
App*Month	-0.001745	0.004108	-0.42	0.6732

(d) Assuming that month = 0, these models predict a selling price of either $969,420 or $1,058,956. The 95% prediction intervals are very wide.

No interaction model:
```
   Fit   SE Fit        95% CI              95% PI
969420  124756  (717991, 1220848)  (717991, 1220848)
```
Interaction model:
```
    Fit   SE Fit       95% CI              95% PI
1058956  245583  (563690, 1554221)  (563690, 1554221)
```

(e) Shown are the residuals for only the no-interaction model; we see no particular causes for concern, except for the observation that one unit sold for much less than predicted by the model (in late 2010).

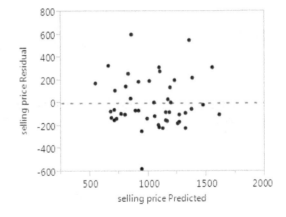

29.53 (a) The estimated equation is given in the Minitab output below. **(b)** To test $H_0: \beta_1 = \beta_2 = \beta_3 = 0$ versus H_a: at least one β_i is not zero, we have $F = 935.67$ and $P < 0.0005$ (ANOVA table below), so we conclude that something in the model is useful. **(c)** The estimated regression parameters, standard errors, t statistics, and P-values are found (in that order) in the Minitab output. **(d)** The distribution of residuals (histogram not shown) is somewhat right-skewed, and the plot of residuals versus fitted values shows a curved pattern (similar to that observed in the previous exercise). **(e)** The model explains $R^2 = 89.0\%$ of the variation in price. **(f)** The estimate of σ is $s = 2592$; this is our estimate of the degree of scatter about the regression formula.

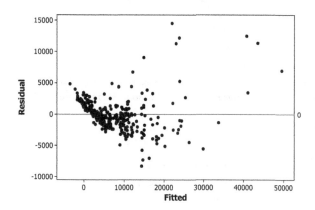

```
The regression equation is
Total Price = 31171 - 11828 Carat - 598 Depth + 408 Carat*Depth

Predictor          Coef   SE Coef        T       P
Constant          31171      4220     7.39   0.000
Carat            -11828      3436    -3.44   0.001
Depth           -598.18     65.47    -9.14   0.000
Carat*Depth      408.45     51.96     7.86   0.000


S = 2591.98    R-Sq = 89.0%   R-Sq(adj) = 88.9%

Analysis of Variance

Source           DF            SS           MS        F       P
Regression        3   18858539949   6286179983   935.67   0.000
Residual Error  347    2331269584      6718356
Total           350   21189809533
```

Exercise **29.55** is a Web-based exercise.

Chapter 30 – More about Analysis of Variance

30.1 PLAN: We compare tip percentages by type of weather report (good, bad, none) using graphs, check conditions for ANOVA, and use the ANOVA F test to compare the population means. SOLVE: Histograms provide little evidence against Normality, although the "none" group has one relatively low tip (10.8%) that might be considered to be an outlier. Tips for good weather reports seem to be higher. The ratio of largest standard deviation (2.388, for none) to smallest standard deviation (1.959, for good) is less than 2. Conditions for the ANOVA F test appear to be met. The output shows that the mean tip for good weather report is higher than the other report group means. The ANOVA is significant: $F = 20.679$, $P < 0.001$. CONCLUDE: The data provide strong evidence that mean tip percentages are not the same for all three groups. It appears that customers receiving a good weather report tip more, on average.

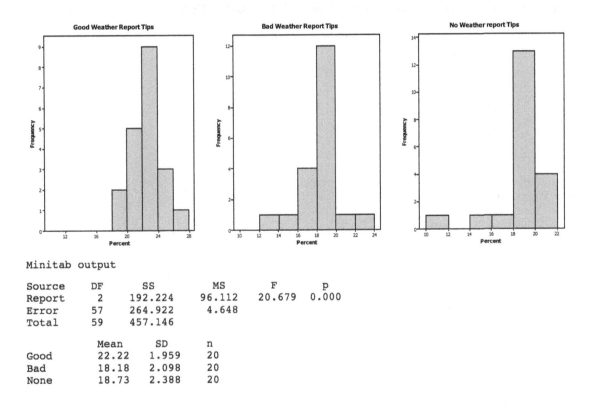

```
Minitab output

Source    DF      SS        MS       F        p
Report    2     192.224   96.112   20.679   0.000
Error     57    264.922    4.648
Total     59    457.146

          Mean    SD       n
Good      22.22   1.959    20
Bad       18.18   2.098    20
None      18.73   2.388    20
```

30.3 PLAN: We compare heart rate in the three groups using graphs, check conditions for ANOVA, and use the ANOVA F test to compare population mean heart rates. SOLVE: The stemplots show some possible mild skewness or outliers, but nothing too drastic. It appears that heart rates are highest with friends present and lowest with pets present. The Minitab ANOVA output below shows that the standard deviations easily satisfy our rule of thumb, and that the differences are highly significant: $F = 14.08$, $P < 0.0005$. CONCLUDE: The data provide strong evidence that mean heart rate differs; specifically, stress (as measured by heart rate) is lowest when a person's dog is present and highest when a friend is present.

	Control	Friend	Dog
5			8
6	2		4
6			58999
7	03		002
7	57	6	59
8	0444	013	
8	777	689	56
9	01	12	
9	9	789	7
10		012	

Minitab output: Analysis of Variance on Rate

Source	DF	SS	MS	F	p
Group	2	2387.7	1193.8	14.08	0.000
Error	42	3561.3	84.8		
Total	44	5949.0			

Individual 95% CIs For Mean
Based on Pooled StDev

Level	N	Mean	StDev	
Ctrl	15	82.524	9.242	(-----*-----)
Friend	15	91.325	8.341	(-----*-----)
Dog	15	73.483	9.970	(-----*-----)

Pooled StDev = 9.208

```
        72.0    80.0    88.0    96.0
```

30.5 (a) With four colors, there are six pairwise comparisons. **(b)** The Tukey procedure indicates yellow attracts the most beetles and is significantly different from green. Both of these are significantly better at attracting beetles than white and blue, which are not different from each other (because they share the letter C). The first set of confidence intervals indicates (family-wise) 95% confidence that the difference $\mu_{Green} - \mu_{Blue}$ is between 7.164 and 25.502 beetles.

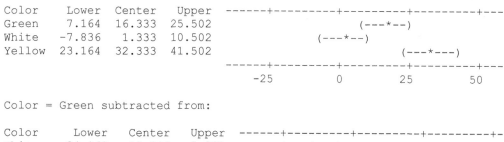

```
Grouping Information Using Tukey Method

Color   N   Mean   Grouping
Yellow  6  47.167  A
Green   6  31.167     B
White   6  16.167        C
Blue    6  14.833        C

Means that do not share a letter are significantly different.

Tukey 95% Simultaneous Confidence Intervals
All Pairwise Comparisons among Levels of Color

Individual confidence level = 98.89%

Color = Blue subtracted from:

Color    Lower   Center   Upper   ------+---------+---------+---------+---
Green    7.164   16.333   25.502                    (---*--)
White   -7.836    1.333   10.502              (---*--)
Yellow  23.164   32.333   41.502                         (---*---)
                                  ------+---------+---------+---------+---
                                      -25        0        25        50

Color = Green subtracted from:

Color    Lower   Center   Upper   ------+---------+---------+---------+---
White  -24.169  -15.000   -5.831        (---*---)
Yellow   6.831   16.000   25.169                     (--*---)
                                  ------+---------+---------+---------+---
                                      -25        0        25        50

Color = White subtracted from:

Color    Lower   Center   Upper   ------+---------+---------+---------+---
Yellow  21.831   31.000   40.169                     (--*---)
                                  ------+---------+---------+---------+---
                                      -25        0        25        50
```

30.7 The estimated contrast is

$\hat{L}_2 = 0(14.833) + 1(31.167) + 0(16.167) + (-1)(47.167) = 31.167 - 47.167 = -16.$

The pooled standard error is $s = 5.672$, so

$$\text{SE}_{\hat{L}_2} = s\sqrt{\frac{0^2}{6} + \frac{1^2}{6} + \frac{0^2}{6} + \frac{(-1)^2}{6}} = s\sqrt{\frac{1}{3}} = 3.2747.$$

A 95% confidence interval for L_2 uses $t^* = 2.086$ from Table C (df = 20):

$\hat{L}_2 \pm t^*\text{SE}_{\hat{L}_2} = -16 \pm 2.086(3.2747) = -16 \pm 6.8311 = -22.8311$ to -9.1689 beetles.

For testing $H_0 : L_2 = 0$ versus $H_a : L_2 \neq 0$, we have $t = \dfrac{\hat{L}_2}{\text{SE}_{\hat{L}_2}} = -4.886$, for which $P <$

0.001. We have very strong evidence that the mean number of beetles trapped by green boards is less than the mean for yellow boards. Specifically, we are 95% confident that, on average, yellow boards catch between 9 and 23 more insects than green boards. Notice that this interval is narrower than the one found in Exercise 30.5 because of a difference in both the standard error and the critical value.

30.9 (a) There is no interaction because the means plots are parallel. **(b)** There is a main effect for herbicide type: Both varieties had higher yields with H2. **(c)** There is a main effect for soybean variety: V2 did better than V1 for all three herbicides.

30.11 (a) The table provided below shows the treatments (with mean status) as a two-way layout. **(b)** Mean conferred status is reported for each group in the aforementioned table, and it is plotted. For men, greater mean status is conferred on expression of anger, while for women the opposite holds. There is obviously strong interaction between sex and expression.

	Gender	
	Male	Female
Anger	6.47	3.75
Sadness	4.05	5.02

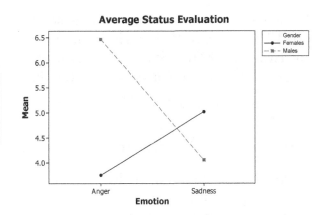

30.13 STATE: What are the effects of sex and housing on counts of social play episodes in hooded rats? PLAN: Plot the sample means and discuss interaction and main effects. Check the conditions for ANOVA inference. Use two-way ANOVA to determine the significance of interaction and main effects. SOLVE: The mean counts are shown in the table below. The means plot suggests little interaction—a weak main effect for housing and a strong main effect for sex. The standard deviations vary from 8.21 to 17.22, which gives a ratio slightly greater than 2. Stemplots (below) show some irregularities and outliers, especially in the two female groups. We proceed with caution. The ANOVA table (below) shows a significant effect of sex ($F = 14.84$, $P < 0.0005$). Housing ($F = 1.70$, $P = 0.199$) and interaction ($F = 0.49$, $P = 0.489$) are not significant. CONCLUDE: The tentative conclusions drawn from the means plot are supported by the ANOVA results: Counts of social play episodes differ significantly by sex, but housing and interaction do not have significant effects.

	MIso	MGp	FIso	FGp
0	788	89		9
1	044		1	
1	7	5689	77	
2	01			
2	799	5		566
3		234	00	24
3			56	6
4			04	4
4		59	5	7
5				23
5			7	
6				
6			7	
7				
7				5

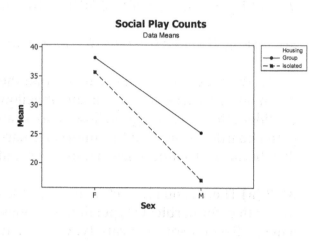

		Sex	
		M	F
Housing	Isolated	17	35.75
	Group	25.25	38.25

Minitab output: Analysis of Variance for Count

Source	DF	Seq SS	Adj SS	Adj MS	F	P
Sex	1	3024.2	3024.2	3024.2	14.84	0.000
Housing	1	346.7	346.7	346.7	1.70	0.199
Sex*Housing	1	99.2	99.2	99.2	0.49	0.489
Error	44	8964.8	8964.8	203.7		
Total	47	12434.8				

30.15 The two-way ANOVA table from the solution to Exercise 30.12 is reproduced below. **(a)** The one-way ANOVA SSG is the sum of the three model sums of squares from the two-way ANOVA: SSG = 11,193.5 + 623.5 + 72.5 = 11,889.5. **(b)** The df for groups for one-way ANOVA is the sum of the three model degrees of freedom: DFG = $1 + 1 + 1 = 3$. Therefore, MSG = $\dfrac{\text{SSG}}{\text{DFG}}$ = 3963.16. MSE = 870.9 is the same as for two-way ANOVA, so $F = \dfrac{\text{MSG}}{\text{MSE}}$ = 4.55. **(c)** There is a significant effect of group: Comparing $F = 4.55$ to an F distribution with df 3 and 44 gives $P = 0.007$. We conclude that time spent in social play differs among the four groups. **(d)** The Minitab one-way ANOVA results below agree with the computations above, up to rounding error.

```
 Minitab output: Two-way ANOVA
 Source         DF    Seq SS      Adj SS     Adj MS       F      P
 Sex             1    11193.5     11193.5    11193.5    12.85  0.001
 Housing         1      623.5       623.5      623.5     0.72  0.402
 Sex*Housing     1       72.5        72.5       72.5     0.08  0.774
 Error          44    38318.4     38318.4      870.9
 Total          47    50208.0
 One-way ANOVA
 Source         DF    Seq SS      Adj SS     Adj MS       F      P
 Group           3    11889.6     11889.6     3963.2     4.55  0.007
 Error          44    38318.4     38318.4      870.9
 Total          47    50208.0
```

30.17 (b) Call the treatments A, B, and C. The three pairwise comparisons are AB, AC, and BC.

30.19 (b) We have enough evidence to conclude that $\mu_1 \neq \mu_2$ but do not have enough evidence to conclude that $\mu_1 \neq \mu_2$ or $\mu_2 \neq \mu_3$. (Remember that, in general, the conclusion of a significance test is that we cannot reject H_0 and *not* that "we are certain that H_0 is true.")

30.21 (c) The other two descriptions are for the main effect of program and the main effect of frequency.

30.23 (c) There are six treatment groups: lo/slow, lo/medium, lo/fast, hi/slow, hi/medium, and hi/fast.

30.25 (c) $s = \sqrt{MSE} = \sqrt{112.5} = 10.61$

30.27 (c) The interaction is not significant at either the 1% or the 5% level ($F = 0.97$, $P = 0.3932$).

30.29 The ANOVA table is shown below. **(a)** The appropriate contrast is $L = \mu_{bihai} - 0.5\left(\mu_{red} + \mu_{yellow}\right)$. **(b)** We wish to test H_0: $L = 0$ versus H_a: $L > 0$. The estimated contrast is $\hat{L} = (1)(47.597) + (-0.5)(39.711) + (-0.5)(36.180) = 9.652$. The pooled standard error is $s = 1.446$, so

$$SE_{\hat{L}} = s\sqrt{\frac{1^2}{16} + \frac{(-0.5)^2}{23} + \frac{(-0.5)^2}{15}} = 0.4337.$$ The test statistic is $t = \dfrac{\hat{L}}{SE_{\hat{L}}} = 22.25$, for which

P is virtually zero. We have overwhelming evidence that mean *bihai* length is greater than the average of red and yellow mean lengths. **(c)** A 90% confidence interval for L uses $t^* = 1.676$ (use df = 50 in Table C):
$\hat{L} \pm t^* SE_{\hat{L}} = 9.652 \pm (1.676)(0.4337) = 9.652 \pm 0.7269 = 8.925$ to 10.379.

```
Minitab output: Analysis of Variance on Length
Source      DF        SS        MS        F         p
Factor       2   1082.87    541.44   259.12    0.000
Error       51    106.57      2.09
Total       53   1189.44
                                      Individual 95% CIs For Mean
                                      Based on Pooled StDev
Level        N      Mean     StDev    ---------+---------+---------+-------
    1       16    47.597     1.213                                 (-*-)
    2       23    39.711     1.799                     (*-)
    3       15    36.180     0.975    (-*--)
                                      ---------+---------+---------+-------
Pooled StDev =   1.446                   38.5      42.0      45.5
```

30.31 (a) We wish to test H_0: $L = 0$ versus H_a: $L > 0$, where the contrast is $L = \mu_1 - 0.25\left(\mu_0 + \mu_{0.5} + \mu_1 + \mu_{1.5}\right)$. **(b)** The estimated contrast is $\hat{L} = -0.17 - 0.25(-6.42 - 5.71 - 1.47 - 13.80) = 6.68$. The pooled standard error is $s = 11.75$, so $\text{SE}_{\hat{L}} = s\sqrt{\dfrac{1^2}{18} + \dfrac{(-0.25)^2}{12} + \dfrac{(-0.25)^2}{14} + \dfrac{(-0.25)^2}{15} + \dfrac{(-0.25)^2}{15}} = 3.187$. The test statistic is $t = \dfrac{\hat{L}}{\text{SE}_{\hat{L}}} = 2.096$, for which $P = 0.0157$. We have fairly strong evidence against H_0, and we conclude that the healing rate under natural conditions is greater than the average of the healing rates under other conditions. **(c)** Contrasts should be formulated before seeing the data.

30.33 (a) The means (in seconds) are shown in the given table. The means plot suggests a strong main effect for housing and a possible (weak) interaction. **(b)** The standard deviations vary from 17.08 to 40.1, which gives a ratio slightly greater than 2. Stemplots (given) show some outliers in the group-housing distributions. We proceed with caution. **(c)** The ANOVA table shows a significant effect of housing ($F = 15.57$, $P < 0.0005$). Sex ($F = 0.27$, $P = 0.605$) and interaction ($F = 0.89$, $P = 0.351$) are not significant. This is consistent with the conclusions from the means plot.

	MIso	MGp	FIso	FGp
0	9	3	8	
1		5		03
2	0469			6
3	4456	89	06678	
4	9		49	6
5	7	5	19	4
6			9	9
7	4	038		28
8				0
9				4
10		9		1
11		3		
12		136		
13				
14				9

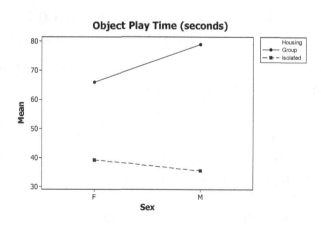

		Sex	
		M	F
Housing	Isolated	35.58	39.33
	Group	79.0	66.0

Minitab output: Analysis of Variance for Time

Source	DF	Seq SS	Adj SS	Adj MS	F	P
Sex	1	256.7	256.7	256.7	0.27	0.605
Housing	1	14735.0	14735.0	14735.0	15.57	0.000
Sex*Housing	1	841.7	841.7	841.7	0.89	0.351
Error	44	41635.6	41635.6	946.3		
Total	47	57469.0				

30.35 (a) The means plot suggests a main effect for application rate (higher application increases leaf necrosis) and a main effect for hybrid (generally, Resistant1 is best, Nonresistant is worst, and Resistant2 is in the middle). There is also an interaction (the lines are not parallel). **(b)** Because seven of the samples have no variation (standard deviation 0), we cannot justify the assumption that the samples come from Normal distributions with a common standard deviation. (Put another way, the largest standard deviation is 17.32, so the largest-to-smallest ratio is undefined—much larger than 2.)

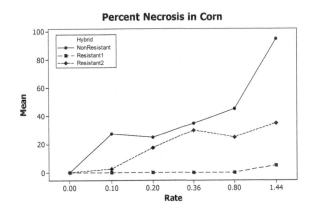

30.37 If μ_i is the mean time for race i, the appropriate contrast is $L = 0.2(\mu_1 + \mu_2 + \mu_3 + \mu_4 + \mu_5) - 0.2(\mu_6 + \mu_7 + \mu_8 + \mu_9 + \mu_{10})$. Based on the sample means (listed in the table on the right), $\hat{L} = 0.9126$ with standard error $SE_{\hat{L}} = 0.4178$. With $t = \dfrac{\hat{L}}{SE_{\hat{L}}} = 2.1841$, we

Race	Mean time	Race	Mean time
1	23.551	6	22.444
2	23.281	7	22.147
3	22.829	8	21.621
4	22.227	9	21.953
5	22.196	10	21.356

have significant evidence that L is different from 0 (the two-sided P-value is 0.0315).

30.39 (a) When we combine the data, there are 12 observations in each group. **(b)** The ANOVA F test is significant at the 5% level: $F = 3.57$, $P = 0.040$. At least one of the three means is different. **(c)** Based on the Tukey confidence intervals, the unfertilized mean is significantly different from the high-fertilizer mean. **(d)** We might consider these groups to represent the population of all tomatoes of the two varieties (normal and mutant), but it is not entirely clear how well these comparisons would apply to members of that population, let alone to other tomatoes.

```
Source   DF      SS      MS      F      P
Fert      2   0.1014  0.0507   3.57  0.040
Error    33   0.4693  0.0142
Total    35   0.5707

S = 0.1193    R-Sq = 17.77%   R-Sq(adj) = 12.78%

                              Individual 95% CIs For Mean Based on
                              Pooled StDev
Level   N    Mean   StDev    ----+---------+---------+---------+-----
   0   12  0.3800  0.1500                      (---------*---------)
  28   12  0.3150  0.1184             (---------*---------)
 160   12  0.2500  0.0785    (---------*---------)
                              ----+---------+---------+---------+-----
                              0.210     0.280     0.350     0.420
Pooled StDev = 0.1193

Grouping Information Using Tukey Method

Fert   N    Mean   Grouping
   0  12  0.3800   A
  28  12  0.3150   A B
 160  12  0.2500     B

Means that do not share a letter are significantly different.

Tukey 90% Simultaneous Confidence Intervals
All Pairwise Comparisons among Levels of Fert

Individual confidence level = 95.91%

Fert =    0 subtracted from:

Fert   Lower   Center   Upper    ---------+---------+---------+---------+
  28  -0.1686  -0.0650  0.0386        (---------*-------)
 160  -0.2336  -0.1300  -0.0264   (-------*--------)
                                  ---------+---------+---------+---------+
                                       -0.12      0.00      0.12      0.24

Fert =   28 subtracted from:

Fert   Lower   Center   Upper    ---------+---------+---------+---------+
 160  -0.1686  -0.0650  0.0386        (--------*-------)
                                  ---------+---------+---------+---------+
                                       -0.12      0.00      0.12      0.24
```

30.41 STATE: Do discourse signaling cues help listeners better comprehend a second language? PLAN: Plot the sample means and discuss interaction and main effects. Use two-way ANOVA to determine the significance of interaction and main effects. SOLVE: The lines in the plot of means are parallel, suggesting no interaction. Both main effects

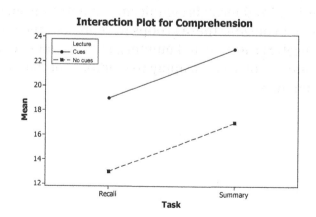

appear to be present: The scores with discourse cues are higher for both tasks, and the summary scores are higher both with and without cues. The ANOVA table confirms that interaction is not significant ($F = 0.005$, $P = 0.943$). Both main effects are highly significant (for lecture, $F = 16.582$, $P < 0.0005$; for task, $F = 7.177$, $P = 0.009$). CONCLUDE: The study demonstrates the effectiveness of discourse cues in improving comprehension in a second language. (The significance of the task main effect does not necessarily mean that the summarizing subjects truly had higher comprehension. It might just indicate that, of the two ways to measure comprehension, subjects score higher when asked for a summary.)

Note: The fact that the interaction F statistic was not exactly 0 tells us that the reported means were rounded; if the lines had been exactly parallel, we would have had $F = 0$. However, based on the small size of F, it is clear that even with unrounded means, the lines would be almost perfectly parallel.

30.43 (a) Based on the one-way ANOVA F test, we cannot conclude that any means are different ($F = 1.93$, $P = 0.148$). Technically, because the ANOVA was not significant, we should not ask for Tukey intervals, but they are included below for reference. They confirm the ANOVA results: All Tukey intervals include 0. **(b)** The two-way ANOVA F tests point to a significant main effect for phosphorus. This conclusion was hidden in the one-way ANOVA, which treats the P and NP groups as unrelated, so it does not allow us to conclude that there are fewer dead leaves with phosphorus.

```
Source   DF       SS     MS     F      P
Group     3    46.38  15.46  1.93  0.148
Error    28   224.50   8.02
Total    31   270.88

S = 2.832   R-Sq = 17.12%   R-Sq(adj) = 8.24%

Individual 95% CIs For Mean Based on
                           Pooled StDev
Level  N    Mean   StDev  ---------+---------+---------+---------+
C      8  11.000   3.742                   (---------*---------)
N      8  10.750   3.240                (---------*---------)
NP     8   8.250   2.315   (---------*----------)
P      8   8.750   1.488     (----------*---------)
                           ---------+---------+---------+---------+
                              8.0      10.0      12.0      14.0
Pooled StDev = 2.832

Grouping Information Using Tukey Method

Group  N    Mean  Grouping
C      8  11.000  A
N      8  10.750  A
P      8   8.750  A
NP     8   8.250  A

Means that do not share a letter are significantly different.

Tukey 90% Simultaneous Confidence Intervals
Individual confidence level = 97.69%
```

```
Group = C subtracted from:

Group    Lower    Center   Upper   --------+---------+---------+---------+-
N        -3.654   -0.250   3.154            (--------*---------)
NP       -6.154   -2.750   0.654   (---------*---------)
P        -5.654   -2.250   1.154     (---------*--------)
                                    --------+---------+---------+---------+-
                                        -3.5      0.0       3.5       7.0

Group = N subtracted from:

Group    Lower    Center   Upper   --------+---------+---------+---------+-
NP       -5.904   -2.500   0.904     (---------*---------)
P        -5.404   -2.000   1.404     (--------*---------)
                                    --------+---------+---------+---------+-
                                        -3.5      0.0       3.5       7.0

Group = NP subtracted from:

Group    Lower    Center   Upper   --------+---------+---------+---------+-
P        -2.904   0.500    3.904             (--------*---------)
                                    --------+---------+---------+---------+-
                                        -3.5      0.0       3.5       7.0
```

Two-Way ANOVA: Dead versus Nitr, Phos

```
Source        DF      SS       MS       F      P
Nitr          1     1.125   1.1250   0.14   0.711
Phos          1    45.125  45.1250   5.63   0.025
Interaction   1     0.125   0.1250   0.02   0.902
Error        28   224.500   8.0179
Total        31   270.875

S = 2.832    R-Sq = 17.12%    R-Sq(adj) = 8.24%
```

30.45 (a) The "means" plot suggests that any interaction is likely to be small; the lines are not quite parallel, but with only one observation per group, we could not expect perfect alignment.
(b) The two-way ANOVA model does not give significant results for either main effect: $F = 12.16$, $P = 0.073$ for brick type, and $F = 5.68$, $P = 0.150$ for firing temperature. While we do not reject either of the

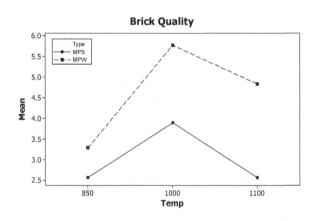

null hypotheses in this case, we have some evidence for a difference based on both factors. A sample size of 1 per group means that our test has low power—the usual problem arising from small samples.

```
Source  DF       SS        MS       F       P
Type     1  3.95282   3.95282   12.16   0.073
Temp     2  3.69130   1.84565    5.68   0.150
Error    2  0.65003   0.32502
Total    5  8.29415

S = 0.5701   R-Sq = 92.16%   R-Sq(adj) = 80.41%
```

Exercise **30.47** is a Web-based exercise.

Chapter 31 – Statistical Process Control

31.1 & **31.3** Answers will vary.

31.5 Possible causes could include alarm not set, had to wait for a train (or traffic), flat tire, spent too much time eating breakfast, and so forth.

31.7 Some examples of special causes that might raise Tayler's time include difficult weather (a particularly hot day or rain, for example), a sore toe, or a mild illness.

31.9 Common causes of variation might include time spent showering, getting dressed, or preparing and eating breakfast. Examples of special causes might include forgetting to set the alarm, encountering (or being in) a traffic accident, waiting for a train, or getting an unexpected phone call before leaving. (These special causes would result in late arrival; it is harder to imagine special causes that might result in early arrival.)

31.11 (a) Center: 11.5 kg; control limits: $\mu \pm 3\dfrac{\sigma}{\sqrt{4}}$ = 11.5 ± 0.3 = 11.2 and 11.8 kg.

(b) The graphs are provided. Points outside control limits are marked with an "X."
(c) Set B is from the in-control process. The process mean shifted suddenly for Set A; it appears to have changed on about the eleventh or twelfth sample. The mean drifted gradually for the process in Set C.

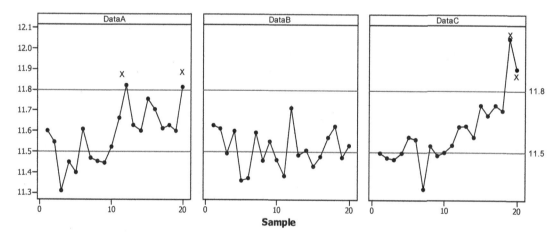

31.13 Because $n = 4$, we have $c_4 = 0.9213$, $B_5 = 0$, and $B_6 = 2.088$. The center line is CL = $c_4\sigma$ = (0.9213)(0.4) = 0.36852; the control limits are LCL = $B_5\sigma$ = 0(0.4) = 0 and UCL = $B_6\sigma$ = (2.088)(0.4) = 0.8352.

31.15 (a) For $n = 5$, we have $c_4 = 0.94$, $B_5 = 0$, and $B_6 = 1.964$, so the center line is 0.11938, and the control limits are 0 and 0.249428. **(b)** The center line is $\mu = 4.22$, and the control limits are $\mu \pm 3\dfrac{\sigma}{\sqrt{5}} = 4.0496$ to 4.3904.

31.17 The new type of yarn would appear on the $\bar{x}$ chart because it would cause a shift in the mean pH. (It might also affect the process variability and therefore show up on the s chart.) Additional water in the kettle would change the pH for that kettle, which would change the mean pH and also change the process variability, so we would expect that special cause to show up on both the $\bar{x}$ and s charts.

31.19 One possible $\bar{x}$ chart is shown, created with the assumption that the experienced clerk processes invoices in an average of 2 minutes, while the new hire takes an average of 4 minutes. (The control limits were set arbitrarily as well.)

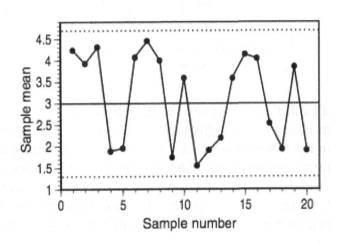

31.21 (a) Average the 20 sample means and standard deviations and estimate μ to be $\hat{\mu} = \bar{\bar{x}} = 275.07$ mV and σ to be $\hat{\sigma} = \bar{s}/c_4 = 34.55/0.9213 = 37.50$ mV. **(b)** In the s chart shown in Figure 31.7, most of the points fall below the center line.

31.23 (a) For the 21 samples, we have $\bar{s} = 0.2786$, so $\hat{\sigma} = \bar{s}/c_4 = 0.2786/0.9213 = 0.3024$; the center line is $\bar{s}$, and the control limits are $B_5\hat{\sigma} = 0$ and $B_6\hat{\sigma} = (2.088)(0.3024) = 0.6313$. Short-term variation seems to be in control. **(b)** For the $\bar{x}$ chart, the center line is 0, and the control limits are $\pm 3\,\hat{\sigma}/\sqrt{4} = \pm 0.4536$. The $\bar{x}$ chart suggests that the process mean has drifted. (Only the first four out-of-control points are marked.) One possible cause for the increase in the mean is that the cutting blade is getting dull.

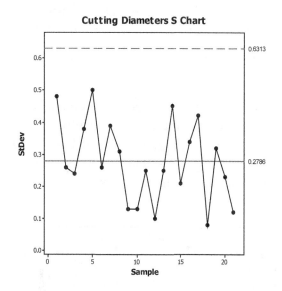

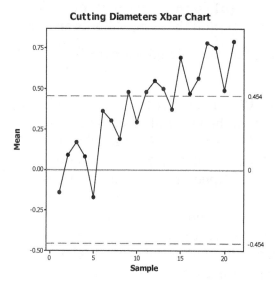

31.25 If the manufacturer practices SPC, that provides some assurance that the monitors are roughly uniform in quality, as the text says, "We know what to expect in the finished product." So, assuming that uniform quality is sufficiently high, the purchaser does not need to inspect the monitors as they arrive because SPC has already achieved the goal of that inspection—to avoid buying many faulty monitors. (Of course, a few unacceptable monitors may be produced and sold, even when SPC is practiced, but inspection would not catch all such monitors anyway.)

31.27 A histogram (provided) or stemplot shows that the number of losses between $6000 and $6500 is noticeably higher than we might expect from a Normal distribution, but otherwise the shape of the graph suggests that the natural tolerances should be fairly trustworthy.

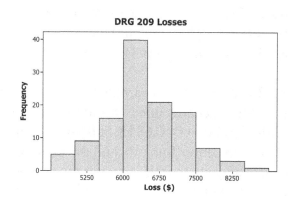

Note: In fact, the smallest and largest losses were $4727 and $8794; these are both within the tolerances, but note that the minimum is quite a bit above the lower limit of the tolerances ($4008). The large number of losses between $6000 and $6500 makes the mean slightly lower and therefore lowers both of the tolerance limits.

31.29 If we shift the process mean to 250 mV, about 99% will meet the new specifications:

$$P\left(150 < X < 350\right) = P\left(\frac{150 - 250}{38.4} < Z < \frac{350 - 250}{38.4}\right) = P\left(-2.60 < Z < 2.60\right) = 0.9906.$$

31.31 Only about 44% of meters meet the specifications. Using the mean (43.4118) and standard deviation (11.5833) found in the solution to Exercise 31.30,

$$P(44 < X < 64) = P\left(\frac{44 - 43.4118}{11.5833} < Z < \frac{64 - 43.4118}{11.5833}\right) = P(0.05 < Z < 1.78) = 0.4426.$$

31.33 (a) For those 10 months, there were 960 overdue invoices out of 28,750 total invoices, so $\overline{p} = \dfrac{960}{28,750} = 0.03339$. **(b)** The center line and control limits are CL = $\overline{p}$ = 0.03339, and $\overline{p} \pm 3\sqrt{\dfrac{\overline{p}(1-\overline{p})}{2875}} = 0.02334$ and 0.04344.

31.35 The center line is $\overline{p} = \dfrac{220}{37,200} = 0.005914$. The control limits are $\overline{p} \pm 3$

$\sqrt{\dfrac{\overline{p}(1-\overline{p})}{1070}} = -0.001118$ to 0.012946, so use LCL = 0 and UCL = 0.0129.

31.37 (b) The center line of an $\overline{x}$ chart should be the target mean.

31.39 (b) The center line for an s chart is $c_4\sigma$. With $n = 4$, $c_4 = 0.9213$.

31.41 (a) $\hat{\sigma} = \dfrac{\overline{s}}{c_4}$, so $\hat{\sigma} = \dfrac{5.1}{0.9213} = 5.5357$. The LCL is $\overline{\overline{x}} - 3\dfrac{\hat{\sigma}}{\sqrt{n}} = 48.4 - 3\dfrac{5.5357}{\sqrt{4}} = 40.1$.

31.43 (a) The UCL is $\overline{p} + 3\sqrt{\dfrac{\overline{p}(1-\overline{p})}{n}}$.

31.45 (a) (ii) a sudden change in the x chart: This would immediately increase the amount of time required to complete the checks. **(b)** (i) a sudden change (decrease) in s or R because the new measurement system will remove (or decrease) the variability introduced by human error **(c)** (iii) a gradual drift in the $\overline{x}$ chart (presumably a drift up, if the variable being tracked is the length of time to complete a set of invoices)

31.47 (a) The percents do not add to 100% because one customer might have several complaints; that is, he or she could be counted in several categories. **(b)** Clearly, the process of creating, correcting, and adjusting invoices should be given top priority because the three most common complaints involved invoices.

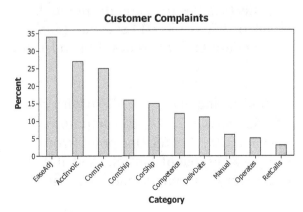

31.49 (a) Use an $\bar{x}$ chart or s chart to monitor Web site availability. **(b)** Use of an $\bar{x}$ chart or s chart is appropriate to track response time. **(c)** Use a p chart to track the percent of Web site changes not properly documented.

31.51 The most common problems are related to the application of the color coat; that should be the focus of our initial efforts.

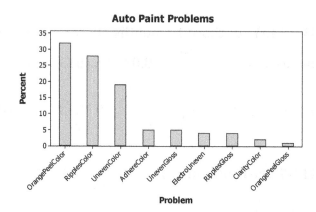

31.53 (a) $\bar{p} = \dfrac{3}{1,000,000} =$ 0.000003. At 4000 pieces per day, we expect $(4000)(0.000003) = 0.012$ defects per day; in a 24-day month, we would expect $(24)(0.012) = 0.288$ defects. **(b)** The center line is CL = $\bar{p}$ = 0.000003.

Assuming that every day we examine all 4000 pieces, LCL = $\bar{p} - 3\sqrt{\dfrac{\bar{p}(1-\bar{p})}{4000}}$ = – 0.00008, which is negative (so we use 0), and UCL = $\bar{p} + 3\sqrt{\dfrac{\bar{p}(1-\bar{p})}{4000}}$ = 0.000085. **(c)**

Note that most of the time, we will find 0 defects, so that $\hat{p}$ = 0. If we should ever find even one defect, we would have $\hat{p}$ = 0.00025 > UCL, and the process would be deemed out of control. It takes a lot of testing to find even one defect.

31.55 Students will have varying justifications for the sampling choice. Choosing six calls per shift gives an idea of the variability and mean for the shift as a whole. If we took six consecutive calls (at a randomly chosen time), we might see additional variability in $\bar{x}$ because sometimes those six calls might be observed at particularly busy times (when a customer has to wait for a long time until a representative is available, or when a representative is on break).

31.57 The outliers are 276 seconds (sample 28), 244 seconds (sample 42), and 333 seconds (sample 46). After dropping those outliers, the standard deviations drop to 9.284, 6.708, and 31.011 seconds. (Sample #39, the other out-of-control point, has two moderately large times, 144 and 109 seconds; if they are removed, s drops to 3.416.)

31.59 We find that $\bar{s}$ = 7.65, so with c_4 = 0.8862 and B_6 = 2.276, we compute $\hat{\sigma}$ = 8.63 and UCL = 19.65. One point (from sample #1) is out of control. (And, if that cause were determined and the point

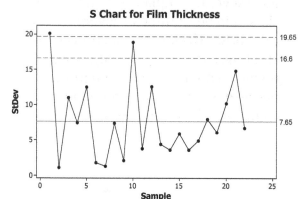

removed, a new chart would have *s* for sample #10 out of control.) The second (lower) UCL line on the control chart is the final UCL, after removing both of those samples (per the instructions in the next exercise).

31.61 (a) Use a *p* chart, with center line $\bar{p} = \dfrac{15}{5000} = 0.003$ and control limits $\bar{p} \pm 3$

$\sqrt{\dfrac{\bar{p}(1-\bar{p})}{100}}$, or 0 to 0.0194. **(b)** There is little useful information to be gained from keeping a *p* chart: If the proportion remains at 0.003, about 74% of samples will yield a proportion of 0, and about 22% of proportions will be 0.01. To call the process out of control, we would need to see two or more unsatisfactory films in a sample of 100.

31.63 is a Web-based exercise.